FULL STRENGTH ANGELS

(NEW WRITING SCOTLAND 14)

Edited by

KATHLEEN JAMIE
and
JAMES McGONIGAL

with Meg Bateman (Gaelic Adviser)

Association for Scottish Literary Studies

Association for Scottish Literary Studies
c/o Department of Scottish History, 9 University Gardens
University of Glasgow, Glasgow G12 8QH

First published 1996

© Association for Scottish Literary Studies
and the contributors

British Library Cataloguing in Publication Data

A CIP record for this book is available
from the British Library

ISBN 0–948877–31–6

Typeset by Roger Booth Associates, Hassocks, West Sussex

Printed by Cromwell Press, Melksham, Wiltshire

CONTENTS

INTRODUCTION

Tobacco smoke (full strength) and angels drift in our domestic air. Ghosts and other echoes shift there too. In a year which has seen the passing of two important Scottish poets, it is appropriate that the salutation of poetic friends or father figures emerges as a central theme in *NWS 14*. Thus, Walt Whitman and Norman MacCaig make their appearance alongside R.D. Laing, and the Roman poet Guisseppe Belli and the Provençal poet Frédéric Mistral enter re-suited in braid Scots claith. There's also what looks like the start of a flyting between two of the younger poets; and an amusing and bemusing evocation by Pete Fortune of how young writers interact 'In an Age of Advanced Communications'.

Far from being inward-looking, a sharp attention is turned firth of these shores. The 'Scottish' vision and voice extends to Iceland, Africa, America, Italy – though we carry our cultural baggage with us on the journey. Alcohol and tobacco are the social drugs most obviously available in the duty-free zone, and also in this volume. Both editors quickly tired of the many contributors who offered sub-Welshian wanderings through an unfocused urban drug scene. We preferred the heady energies of female Humphrey Bogarts, or of Cuchulain out the back.

Throughout, we also discovered a welcome emphasis on new life: on bairn rhymes and child's play; on the features of offspring, both strange and familiar; on the peppermint sharpness of adolescent awakenings; or moments when young parents recall the 'full strength', as well as the flaws, of their own fathers and mothers. Angels can reveal themselves at such moments of growth, and sometimes do.

This year, as ever, we had the problem of attempting to balance new talent with established voices, and all the differing energies of dialect, language and gender which give new Scottish writing its excitement and density. We found enough good work to fill a volume twice this size. To those whose poems and stories are still adrift in air, not here, we wish for happier landings next time.

Kathleen Jamie
James McGonigal

NEW WRITING SCOTLAND 15

Submissions are invited for the fifteenth annual volume of *New Writing Scotland,* to be published in 1997, from writers resident in Scotland or Scots by birth or upbringing. Poetry, drama, short fiction or other creative prose may be submitted but not full-length plays or novels, though self-contained extracts are acceptable. The work must be neither previously published nor accepted for publication and may be in any of the languages of Scotland.

Submissions should be typed on one side of the paper only and the sheets secured at the top-left corner. Each individual work should be clearly marked with the author's name and address.

Submissions should be accompanied by two stamped addressed envelopes (one for a receipt, the other for return of MSS) and sent by **31 January 1997 (not before November 1996)** to:

Catherine Mc Inerney
Managing Editor, NWS
ASLS
c/o Dept of Scottish History
9 University Gardens
University of Glasgow
Glasgow G12 8QH
Tel: 0141 330 5309

Linda Anderson

PANDROPS

Of all my friends from school I remember Janice the best. For a while she was my best friend but that's not the reason.

We were thirteen. It was July, the school holidays and that weekend we were going to Kilgreggan to Guide Camp. We were catching the boat from Gourock. There were twenty of us. We were told to meet under the clock under the big glass dome of the station. My dad left me at the entrance and I ran down the echoing glass tunnel, as if I was late, my bag hitting my legs. The sun shone through the glass roof and I was hot. The tunnel of light ended at Miss McBeath.

The stairs from the pier to the boat were slimy green. I remember looking down and thinking about slipping slowly between the rotten planks into the dark water. The metal rail shook under my tight grip. It's funny. They wouldn't allow that now. The rickety stairs and the rusted rail. Then I covered my fear with laughter, now I know I have vertigo and I wasn't just a coward.

When we first got a car, a wee green Morris Minor, we drove out on a Sunday just for the fun of it. My dad would drive along Greenock pier. We were miles from the edge but I was sick with fear all the time. At least when you're older you can say so. No, I don't want to drive along the pier because I suffer from vertigo.

Miss McBeath moaned at us most of the journey across but we didn't care. You can't spoil a journey like that. We sat at the very front. The way the water whipped over the front of the small boat and made us scream. The taste of salt on our tongues. Like ready salted crisps.

Every time the boat hit a small wave we screamed, showing off to the old man in the wee cabin and the boy who helped with tying up at the pier. The boy was a bit older than us, not much. I remember his hands because they were oily round the nails. I've always looked at hands, men's hands. I discovered when I was in my twenties that I had to go out with hands that were big and square but looked as if they could touch gently. I don't like soft hands on men and I hate filed nails and pinky rings. Hands are important. They don't have to be clean but they have to be right.

The water at Kilgreggan pier had a bit of a swell on and the boy had to help us step over the side. I remember he wiped his hand first on his blue jersey and his face flushed at the touch of us.

We stood outside the shop while Miss McBeath and the other Leader went to order the milk and bread. Some of the local boys came along and shouted at us from across the street. One of them looked like the boy from the boat but brave now. When Miss McBeath came out they walked away.

We set off along a dirt track up a hill. The hedge on either side was high. Catriona was breathing funny so I had to stop with her for a while until she got her breath back. I think she had asthma but she never said anything about it. We were behind the others now. I told her not to hurry, it didn't matter. I could see Janice's red hair in the distance anyway.

There was a noise in the hedge beside us and one of the boys, not the one from the boat, stuck his head over and shouted something. It sounded like 'Fuck you,' but I told Catriona to ignore it. My heart was pounding but I wasn't frightened. It did cross my mind that at the next gate one of them might show us his willy like that stupid man at the Larkfield shops. I told Catriona not to look round, it just encouraged them.

When we caught up with Miss McBeath she was making everyone walk in twos and we had to put our berets back on. Janice hated that beret. She made a face at me and pinned it on the side of her head. I saw Miss McBeath look over but she wasn't in the mood to argue. The other Leader didn't care. She just did what Miss McBeath said.

The hedge on either side of the dirt track became trees. The nearer we got to the end of the road, the thicker the trees became. We were walking through a tunnel and all the time the light seeping through onto our shoulders.

The gate to the field was closed. We scrambled onto the bars and looked in. What can I say about the field? A green womb of a place. The sun dripping through the leaves dancing on the grass. In shafts of light, tiny flies billowed in clouds. And the smell of the place. A thick heady smell of damp earth. I could smell it growing.

It made me scared, scared and excited at the same time.

The tents were in a high pile in the middle. Miss McBeath made us sit round her and she gave us our orders. We scurried about like ants. We had practised the tent in the back garden already but we pretended not to be sure, shouting 'Miss McBeath, is this right?' every five minutes. After we put the tent up, our group – Janice, me, Catriona and Kirsty – were told to dig the toilets. I'm sure it was because Miss McBeath was annoyed at Janice's beret. We didn't mind. We went down to the bottom of the field with the spades.

'You have to dig deep or else!' Kirsty held her nose.

'It's disgusting,' said Catriona. 'I won't be able to go all weekend.'

'In France,' Janice said, 'they have bogs like this in... well everywhere.'

'No.' I couldn't believe that. Janice was always telling us things like that. She told me there was no God, for example, and that there had once been a volcano in Edinburgh. I didn't believe her, especially about God.

We looked down into the holes and giggled. The holes gaped back at us in anticipation.

Catriona straddled over one. 'What do you do with your knickers?' she said.

God!

We exploded in laughter at the thought.

Janice never really worked at the holes, not really, or the tent. But when Miss McBeath appeared she always looked busy. It didn't make Miss McBeath any less suspicious.

'Have you done your bedroll, Janice?'

Janice always had an answer. 'Just starting that Miss McBeath.'

When we finished our tent, we flattened the ground sheet, threw our sleeping bags in and crept inside.

I loved it. The way the sun danced on the green canvas and dappled it like the field. If you put your hand on the canvas you could feel the heat of the sun. And the smell had followed me in. Warm grass. You could hear it rustle under the ground sheet when you moved. We put our sleeping bags along the sides. I wanted to go to bed right away.

Miss McBeath told us to go and get 'freshened up' before tea. The washrooms were in the opposite corner from the toilets or latrines as Miss McBeath called them. You had to

pour some cold water into a basin and splash it under your
arms. No one wanted to take off their shirt. I opened three
buttons and poked a wet hand with a rub of soap on it, then
stuffed in my towel and dried myself.

I was sharing my basin with Janice. Janice waited until I
was finished with the water and then unbuttoned her shirt and
took it off. She pulled the bra straps off her shoulders and
pulled the bra down to her waist and leaned over the basin.

Her breasts were big and creamy white. The ends were
pink circles. I remember wanting to touch one. I'd never seen a
real breast before. One you could cup in your hand. One that
would weigh something.

I was staring. Although the others were behind me I knew
they were staring too. Janice ignored us and rubbed soap on
her facecloth and carefully circled the breasts, then lifted her
towel and patted them dry.

'Watch this,' she said, and lifted one in each hand and
pointed the pink eyes right at us.

In those days, bras were made of white cotton. The cups
were concentric stiffened circles that ended in a point. Except
no one could fill that point, no one was that shape so the point
curved inwards, a concave. Janice had finished tucking the
breasts inside the cups. Even she didn't fill those end points. She
reached in her toilet bag and pulled out a packet of pandrops.
She opened the packet and took out two pandrops and pushed
one down into the tip of each white cup, popping it forward.

'Keep these warm for later,' she said and we laughed. I
turned away. My face was pink and in my heart was the sharp
green stab of envy.

After tea we sat on the ground round the fire, our knickers
damp from the grass.

'We'll get piles from this,' Catriona whispered in my ear.

We sang 'Land of the Silver Birch, Home of the Beaver' in
three parts. It was my favourite but my mind wasn't on it. I
was wondering what it felt like to roll over in bed with breasts
that size and I wanted to be in my sleeping bag, lying in the
tent in the dark, thinking.

Later on:

'We all have one you know.' Janice was the only one who
didn't whisper.

There was a short silence and then Kirsty's voice said.
'What d'you mean?'
'We all have a *v..u..l..v..a.*' Janice said the word carefully making it longer and sharper than it was.

When the word finally escaped her lips it rose above us and hung there waiting for somebody brave enough to pluck it down. You see we all knew if we asked for more that's exactly what Janice would give us. More. Then things would have to be faced. Things would have to be thought about.

'What's a *vulva*?' This time the word was staccato.

I tried to guess the owner of the voice. Was it still Kirsty? My heart was beating faster. I laid my hand on my chest looking for the suggestion of a curve.

'I thought a vulva was a car.'

The puzzled voice brought screams of hysterical laughter, while the word floated away beyond our derision.

'Shssssh. Miss McBeath will hear us,' I said.

We smothered our laughter with the sleeping bags.

'Catriona! Don't be stupid!' said Janice. 'You're thinking of a *volvo*.'

We felt Catriona shrink back in embarrassment and sent our waves of comfort into the darkness, but Janice held us now, close to her, like the pandrops.

'A *vulva*,' she said, 'is a secret place in women, that men like, because it's moist and inviting.' The words were chanted like a poem committed to memory.

We thought about that. I remember thinking it sounded like the field to me.

'Where. Where is it?' Catriona had returned, undefeated.

'Between your legs of course.'

I felt my legs move together, the sharp knee bones grind against one another. So there was more than the softness of heavy breasts.

'Does Miss McBeath... have one?'

There was an intake of breath. It was something I wanted to ask myself. Kirsty's forthrightness impressed me.

'Of course.' Janice was matter of fact. We were beginning to bore her with our silly questions. She yawned loudly and turned on her side. 'She's probably playing with it right this minute.'

I closed my eyes and tucked my hands under my pillow to stop them from slipping between my legs and tried not to think about Miss McBeath.

The next day was Sunday and we had to go to church.

Janice pinned up her long thick auburn hair in a bun on top of her head.

'You won't get your beret on that,' I said. 'Miss McBeath will go mad.'

Janice reached up and patted the bun, then pinned the beret jauntily on one side. The blue material of her shirt pulled itself tightly across the cotton pyramids. I noticed the pointy ends and wondered if the pandrops were still there.

We began to line up in twos. I tried to get with Catriona, knowing I would be included in Miss McBeath's wrath, but my luck was out. Catriona and Kirsty were already together at the front.

'Janice McVeigh. Put your beret on properly.'

Janice looked innocent. 'I can't get it any flatter Miss McBeath, my hair's too thick. If you like I'll take my hair down again but it'll take me five minutes.'

Miss McBeath tutted, her lips thin. 'We've no time now, Janice. We'll be late for church.'

A green gleam of triumph shone in Janice's eyes.

We marched in twos down the leafy lane.

At the bottom of the lane three of the boys sat on a fence, waiting for us. The boy with the blue jumper was there. I remembered his hands and looked down. I wondered if his jumper still smelled of the sea. Everyone stopped talking. I suddenly felt silly with my beret and my blue tie and my brass badge. And I kept thinking about things like standing over the toilet hole and what we spoke about in the tent the night before.

The boys started to wolf whistle.

Miss McBeath and the other Leader marched on, ignoring them. Janice slowed down, slanting her eyes towards the boys then away again.

'Nice baps,' the boy with the blue jumper said. The other two laughed.

Janice stopped. Suddenly we were left behind as the rest squashed past, anxious to get away. Janice was staring at the boy in the blue jumper. I tried to walk on.

'Come on Janice.' I said, tugging her arm.

She'd begun to unbutton her shirt. The boy's face changed. His hands let go of the fence and he sprung down. He was close now. I could smell oil and salt from him. A flush began to spread up his cheek.

Janice slipped her right hand inside her open shirt.

'Give me your hand,' she said.

The fingers were thick and the nails circled black.

'Here,' she said, dropping the warm white pearl into his hand, 'have a pandrop.'

Gerry Cambridge

WATER

I venture out at midnight
for water at an outside tap,
my bucket and my kettle
light as air. How the clouds
have vanished and the moon
and constellations
shine up there, an audience
in jewels and hush
gazing from the balconies. Orion
and the fainter Pleiades,
the Plough directly overhead;
nothing between all these
and upturned face but space,
clear billions of empty miles.
The moon and its dead seas
is sharp within my eye. Here
the water drums into the bucket, its
sound altering as it fills.
With heaviness in left hand
and in right, careful lest it spills,
under the bright
amphitheatre, I
trudge back to a square
of light, its room lined
with workings of the mind,
with lingual astronomies,
closing the door
on the simple night.

A WHITMANIAN REPLY (after his sestina)
for David Kinloch

Hearing you read out your poems on a dreich night in Glasgow,
    making the *CCA* a centre of the whole pubbed riotous city,
writing of poets who turned back in fear from the open
    Whitmanian road to sonnets of such insignificance not
    even a microscope shows them,
I thought: *let him away with that? Never! Carnaptious and*
    havering scunner!
O where are the modern free versers with a droplet of
    Whitman's rhythmical energy,
rhythm that's the root of the universe, with metre its regular
    partner;
or of the orbic flex of his balls, singing the paean testicular,
    jetting his love-juice abundantly over the umbrellæd masses
detumescent and muttering curses?

Chopped prose, and I say – what is that?
Meanings obscurest to all but the most intimate friends – what
    are they?
I say I have more in common with Whitman than any free
    verser, in a time of sonnets he wrote rhythmical free verse
    based on the prose in the Bible,
in a time of free verse based not, alas, on Biblical prose I write
    sonnets, quatrains, and some ballads.

I sing of the forms wholehearted and sensual, I sound my
    chirruping invite over the lipsticks of the world.
Hearty, eating and drinking, if you want me again look for me
    among the suspenders.
Amphibrach, dimeter, caesura and pæon, I lie and loaf at my
    ease among the prosodic textbooks, all of which I ignore.

Cunninghamhead is as much a centre as Glasgow,
My cat has come in with the chill of the whole Universe on her
    fur, maiowing for food,
The Pleaides sparkle in the autumn night through the clear
    skylight in the roof of my caravan, the dole has just sent
    me a summoning letter –
I tramp through the puddles to sign on,

Mr Cambridge, a young girl says, with a minister's thumb at
        the base of her neck,
will you go on a training scheme, we have lots of places,
        (plenty of chances for drowning in paper,
and all of small meaning in our fudged-up bureaucracy)?
Christ, I'm a writer of sonnets I say, *and writing loads now*,
        and I say that to be a writer of sonnets is noble,
and that there is little greater than a writer of sharp clean
        sonnets.

John Cameron

WHAT PRICE PEDIGREE?

For the first time I had been left in charge of the farm. The Boss and his sons, John and Jim, had gone to buy a new stock bull and the ladies had gone with them. They had all gone partly because car outings were very few due to wartime petrol rationing and partly because it was a semi social visit. They were going to nearby Lessnessoch Farm, famed for its pedigree Ayrshire cattle. John's ambition was to be in the top league and the purchase of a Lessnessoch bull was a step in that direction. He knew the bull he wanted. It had a great pedigree, but I didn't like his choice as it was nearly all white with just some light brown round its face and shoulders. I much preferred more colour, particularly that dark roan red found in some Ayrshires. But, as John said, colour was less important than pedigree and conformation (shape) and he knew.

As it was the dairyman's day off, my main job was to feed the young beasts and the bulls. That kept an eye on things till the family returned for the milking. It seemed a dawdle. Whistling furiously, I started off in jubilant form. How many fourteen year old townie boys are left in charge of a pedigree dairy farm? I made the battles, tight bundles of hay, for the bull boxes. I chopped the mangolds for the heifers. Now to feed the heifers, a daunting task. They were tied up in their byre, in pairs, during the winter months. Normally they were let out for exercise during the day, but at weekends everybody got a rest. Shit, no other name quite fits, is a dominating element on a dairy farm. High yielding cows not only eat more, they shit more as well. And it's not just the cows. There is bull shit, calf shit, heifer shit, horse shit and more. Everything smells of shit, although as with other smells, once you smell of shit you can no longer detect it. Others, outside the farm, like my aunt in town, could.

Well, the heifers' byre was the shit Mecca; they were covered, the wall was covered, windows and doors were spattered and as for the floor … What floor, there was only straw and shit of indeterminate depth – all to be shovelled out into box carts to the fields in spring.

I started feeding the heifers. One wire basket of mangolds between each pair. How I hated forcing myself between them to put the mangold in their head troughs – kicking rear hooves, shitty arses, swishing tails that caught the face, jerking snorting horned heads and the sheer physical force of their bodies. Still, soon it was done. Now for the bulls. That was different.

The bulls were exciting, partly because of the danger they threatened and partly because of their sexuality. At fourteen the sight of the massive stock bull mounting a cow; the snorting, scuffling of hooves, and the flashing in and out of its long red penis was enough to engender very erotic feelings.

The bulls were kept in individual pens or boxes in a large, airy shed, with the boxes opening on either side of a central passage. The old stock bull, Bargower Ace, was first on the right. He was massive, and bad tempered; spending his hours, between serving cows, tied by the nose to a run rail, pawing his front hooves and bellowing, either because he wanted more sex or was getting far too much. I threw his battle of hay over the wall. I wasn't going in there for anything. Only John did that, usually armed with a hay fork. John was one of my heroes. The next box contained the younger stock bull, less well developed and better tempered, but not to be trusted either. His hay was also thrown in.

Further down the line I became bolder, opening each door and placing the hay in the heck. Now I was amongst bull calves and heifers, including one very special young lady. She was the daughter of our best cow – a past winner of the Glasgow Dairy Show – and her conformation indicated she was going to be like her mother. She was in the box because she had come into heat prematurely and John was anxious to avoid any accidental pregnancy. His plan was to get her mated with the new bull from Lessnessoch. Hopefully she would have a bull calf fit to fetch a big price at the big annual bull sales. Her mother was called Queen Elizabeth so naturally she was called Princess Elizabeth.

I opened the door of the Princess's box, hay under arm. The next moment I was flat on my back wondering what had happened. The Princess was out the door and running. I picked myself up and tore after her. She turned through a half open gate into a field of oats, making high bellowing noises, going full pelt. Answering bellowings from ahead suddenly made it all too apparent where she was headed. The young bulls were in the holm below, fattening up for the autumn sales. Their lives as stock bulls were still ahead and they had so far spent the summer mounting each other in constant practice for their future careers. Running towards them eagerly was not only the real thing, but the last word in bovine pulchritude. The Princess cleared the dyke in one and was in amongst them. After the briefest of sniffings the bulls began their orgy. Their bad manners not allowing any one of them peace for long and the Princess being still on the move, only a modicum of sperm appeared to be getting in the right place, but probably enough. I was frantic. I ran behind them laying on with my stick, somewhat hampered by my own considerable erection which was painful against my dungarees. Then the Princess stopped. Thankfully she had a halter round her neck. I moved to her head and grabbed the rope, only to realise that stopping had allowed the biggest bull, a strong dark roan, to mount and enter her properly. I hit his nose with my stick and pulled on the rope. He slid off allowing me to drag the heifer some yards before the next bull had a go. In this manner we slowly worked our way across the field and eventually reached the gate. I got her through without the bulls who were beginning to tire. Poor Princess Elizabeth, instead of the well planned courtship with a famous sire, she had been gang banged by five motley youngsters. As for John, he would now have a nondescript calf worth a few pounds for veal instead of a moneyspinner. I had been left in charge only to have this happen. What could I do?

At last I regained the bull boxes and tied the Princess firmly to the heck. She was exhausted and plastered with sperm. I got a bucket of hot water, some disinfectant and a large syringe I found on the medical shelf. Then, standing on a milking stool I syringed the disinfected water as far and as often up her vagina as I could. Perhaps that would kill the sperms. Then I washed her down and dried her as best I could.

As I was leaving the farm in two days to start school I decided unless John noticed anything that night I would say nothing. He didn't and I duly left, much relieved, only hoping my syringing had worked. I didn't see anyone from the farm for over a year. My career at boarding school now alternated with holidays working in the warehouse of the family seed business. Then one day I met John in the High Street. After a suitable exchange of pleasantries I asked him if the Princess had been mated as planned. 'Och yes,' he replied. 'We brought the new bull home from Lessnessoch the week after you left and put her to him – and she's had a braw bull calf.'

'Great,' I said. 'You should get a good price for it at the big bull sale.'

'No, no,' he answered. 'We're no selling, we're going to keep him as our stock bull. He's got great conformation and strength. Only funny thing – he hasn't got the sire's colouring – he's got lots of dark roan, must get that from the dam's side way back.'

Dam's side, my foot, I thought, my mind flashing back to that hectic afternoon in the holm field and to Elizabeth the Princess and the pauper – the young dark roan bull. It looked like the future herd was going to be coloured according to MY taste after all. What price pedigree, as they say?

Anna Crowe

THE WINDOW-CLEANERS

arrive in a clatter of ladders –
men in boots, with cloths and buckets
and aprons, tools in pockets,
who have the look of mediaeval cathedral-builders;

who climb as though to the clerestory
up to our second-floor windows,
where they proceed to douse
the glass, erasing one month's history

of weather. These are the same who, sober-
suited, rang this Christmas
morning to bear witness
on our doorstep, pressing *The Watchtower*

into reluctant hands. Now, they scour
each pane as though it were
a soul, splashing water
with rough baptismal ardour.

Haloed in soap, close to the telegraph-wires'
dismal humming,
they'll greet the Second Coming
of the Lord. Till then, regular

as rain, they rise like messengers
from an unsullied Eden –
poised above frozen gardens,
grave men in woolly hats whom light transfigures.

THE PATTERN OF OUR DAYS

Days when we wake to the heron in its tree
we cancel everything,
home in along low, level shafts of light
to the dagger-like beak where it vanishes
under feathered membrane.
A snow-flurry as the ruffled down subsides.

Days that take on the pattern of plumage
as other lives brush us, forcing
minuscule shifts; imperceptible, some of them,
as when a campion withers in Spinkie Den
and yet more eider join the pied flock
below the Castle; or cheerfully exhibitionist
like the firm of joiners extending their own shed
beside the car-park.

Audible patterns you need to listen hard for.
The one o'clock clicking of snibs
as departmental secretaries hurry away for lunch;
just detectable through those hymns
played on the bells up in the tower,
that drop on the town like rich and gloomy treacle.

Days that coax us on to the parched grass
to eat our lunch and let the wall – that lovely curve
of rosy, mellow brick that we look down on
from your office ordinarily, occlude us.
The once-espaliered pears, too, have broken free
and gone a little wild, making a rampant shade.

Time to bite on a spring-onion
and picture the screen-saver on your Mac
generating its random doodles,
building patterns intricate as snowflakes.
With nobody there to watch, it fills up
every bit of space with coloured pixels
then wipes it clean and starts all over.
Dancing all by itself like the young
dancing-apprentice in the Turveydrops' kitchen,
or even Billy Idol. Leaving us
to imagine the rest of the pattern
and colour it in.

Alex Cluness

IN THE THULE BAR, LERWICK

In da Thule time stops
Milk turns ta cream
Marriage ta divorce
An shoppin bags
Rustle
An get left ahint
Laek da memory
O dat time
Da days afore drink
Whin even da simplest
Things wir still simple
Afore da half bottle
Clinked
Against aa da cans
On da cowld rod hom

WINTER

Winter arrives as profoond regret
A lingerin waant
A desire if you laek
Fur things ta be different
Or no ta hiv happened
Fur some een ta still be dere
An things ta be da sam
Da wy dat dey wir

It's clearly depressive dis feelin
November ushers im in
Says hit wis you dat did it
A'll juist laeve you wi it
An December laachs
Wi wind an snaa
Ta mak you think mair on it
Saften you up
Fur January
An Up Helly Aa
An da big despair
Juist afore February
Blissful, forgetful February
Da thaw

Anne Donovan

LOAST

It's thon tree ootside the bedroom windae; overhangin branches fill the sky, big black burds nest in it, swoopin by lik enemy planes. It waves aboot in the wind an muddies the light and things move aboot. You put them in the drawer an they turn up in the wardrobe so you blame Agnes; it must be her, there's naebdy else here, but she says *it wisny me* and gies you wanny her looks that makes you want tae greet. Words, too, keep gettin loast inside yer heid somewhere. You're lookin at sumpn that you know the word fur and you're rummlin aboot inside yer heid, inside aw that cottonwool stuff that seems tae float aboot inside yer heid nooadays, but you canny fun it. Somebdy's moved that too. Your words trail aff then you clear your throat an say, *thingummy* or *ye know*, lik an ordinary person that's jist forgotten a wurd fur a minute. So they try tae guess the wurd an you say *that's it*, even if it's no, jist so's you can finish the sentence. An you wish you'd never said anythin in the furst place, and mibby next time you'll no bother.

Maisty the time you don't need tae bother anyway, there's just you an Agnes and you haveny much to say tae each other after aw these years. She never had any patience wi your conversation even before the words started tae get loast in your heid, she'd raither have read a book or sumpn than listen tae you jabberin oan lik a daft wee burdie. An years ago it didny matter for you went tae your work then oot wi your pals, an Jean and her man came visitin wi the nieces and nephews; then awy a sudden there jist seemed tae be you an Agnes, on your ain, no really likin each ither that much, jist here thigither, lik two auld bits a left-ower furniture.

An you hate this hoose but you canny get away fae it because she won't let you; you've hated it fur years, wi its cauld rooms and ugly wallpaper and uncomfortable chairs, but she'll no move. You depend on her noo, you canny dae things on your ain any mair, lik go the messages or take the bus intae toon, because you keep lossin things. You've loast the words tae say tae the bus driver an you get mixed up wi the money; it looks like bits a paper to you, funny wee scrumply bits a paper in your purse. Sometimes you feel lik takin it oot an throwin it roon the place, lettin it fly in every direction lik pee-the-beds blown by the wind, for whit use is it to you noo? You canny buy anythin you want wi it any mair, because there is nothin you want. All you want is to get back tae bein yoursel, an you know that money canny dae that.

It's funny when you think of how important it used tae be to you, that money at the endy the week in a wee broon envelope. You felt lik a millionaire gaun tae the shops on a Saturday and buying sumpn tae wear fur the dancin or jist sittin in the cafe, drinkin coffee an watchin folk walk aboot the street. Fur you were aye turned oot lovely in thae days, everbdy said so; you loved bright colours lik yella an red an emerald green an you had everythin matchin, bags an shoes and beads. When there was nights oot fae the office you aye hud the nicest rigoot. You used tae make yer ain claes tae, an your fingers were that neat and clever, whizzin alang on that old black Singer machine.

But noo you look in the mirror an you canny see yoursel any mair, jist a wee loast shape, faded away in the distance, the mirror misty an milky as though somebdy hus smeared it wi poalish an forgotten tae rub it aff. An you canny really be boathered wi your body any mair, disny seem lik your body, it's hardly worth the trouble of gettin it washed and dressed, for who sees you noo anyway, except if you huv tae go tae the doactor.

You like gaun tae the doactor an you spend a loaty time gettin ready fur him; havin a bath, even puttin on powder and lipstick, it's the preparation you like best really, to have sumpn tae prepare fur. An you like sittin in the waitin room watchin the other patients for they smile at you but usually they don't talk, or if they dae it's no difficult, no a real conversation that you huv tae answer. *No as cauld the day. Naw. It's that wee wumman doacter that's oan. Oh aye.* It's enough tae nod and smile an you can still do that right enough, even you. Sometimes there's weans in the waitin room and you've aye liked weans, especially wee lassies; you like their soft hair an the nice colours they wear, even though they don't wear frocks nooadays they're still lovely. They remind you of your nieces when they were wee, when you used tae buy them things then sometimes they stayed ower at the weekend and you would watch them sleepin, breathin that deep as only weans kin. Once when you were oot wi Helen, buyin her a special frock, the assistant thoat she wis your daughter and she said, *Oh, she's no ma mammy, she's my auntie,* and you felt hurt for a minute, but she was only tellin the truth after aw.

It's no the same though, havin a niece insteid y a daughter, fur a daughter would visit you every week, no wanst every few months lik Helen. A daughter would come tae the doactors wi you an explain things tae him, a daughter wouldny let you go on your ain an get all mixed up wi your wurds tae you burst oot greetin, a daughter would make them do sumpn aboot it insteid y gieing you pink and yella pills that you forget to take and you don't know whit they're fur anyhow. A daughter would dae that.

A daughter would be saft wi you, no hard an fierce lik a sister, she's so hard on you noo, you don't remember her bein so hard on you before. Sometimes you look at her hunched over the newspaper and see a big black crow, pointy and jaggy, and wonder whit happened tae the sister you used tae go dancin wi, gigglin ower the sodjers thegither. Thae boys, hunners of them there wis, brave and smart in their khaki, but they got loast tae, they never came back, an efter the war there wereny enough to go roon an there were three sisters; you couldny expect them aw tae get men. Jean wis the wan that goat a man, a good man, hud tae be a man for yous aw, fixin things roon the hoose lik a man dis, quiet wi calm, steady hauns.

If he wis here that tree would never huv grown sae high, bloackin oot the light. He would huv cut thae branches back an you wouldny keep lossin things in this room, but noo you huv tae get workmen in and she disny like payin for anythin an the cooncil are that slow. There was that tap that kept drippin aw night; it was that loud you thoat it hud goat oot the bathroom and moved inside yer heid, but it's sorted noo. An they're comin the day the men, tae fix the tree, and when aw the branches are cut aff, the light will come intae this room, again and these shadows will go. Mibby then you'll stop lossin things.

Bill Duncan

CROSSING THE PENTLAND FIRTH

horizon at top of window

heave   Hoy

horizon at bottom of window

lurch

paperback at left hand side of table

pull

paperback at right hand side of table

push

side   to   side

up

down

STROMNESS AHOY!

ONE ORKNEY MORNING

frost	fulmar
snow	swan
sun	skua
ice	oystercatcher
cold	crow
rain	raven
sleet	storm petrel
wind	whimbrel
hail	*harrier*

John Duffy

FULL STRENGTH
(for David)

My father made stones whistle,
skiting them across the flat
frozen loch, the whine of each
bounce tapering in the distance;

that was the fifties when spanners,
books, kettles, footballs disappeared
weekly into the throats of ostriches
in comics. By Parkhead Forge,

Guinness glass snug in its gullet,
the bird grinned at the zookeeper
on the high hoarding. *Do they really
swallow things?* He told me something.

Dark stripes like iron bars, a tiger
of stillness succeeded to this space
above the traffic, beside the huge
shed of hammers, chains, growling

furnace. This was the biggest place
I knew; it was where my father grew.
He explained the work of casting,
and how in Colville's, he had fired

explosive bolts at plates of steel,
and sifted fragments that might still
explode, or cut, or burn. He left
that job. Full Strength was what he smoked,

he let me sip dark stout, bitter taste
for men. This year I will be fifty;
my son brings me a gift, a tin picture-
ostrich, keeper, hidden pint –

he has remembered me telling him
all this, when I stood in the street, light
shining from forge and tiger,
his strong hand to hold, the lurch

of trams taking the bend, whining
uphill. Today I throw a stone across ice,
it casts a deeper note than I remember,
drops in pitch with every bounce,

with every bounce.

HERO

and stayed there with his head on his paws; and wild,
savage, fierce, rude, surly and pugnacious was he who
was there – **Tain Bo Cualinge**

first hints of night chill this place it is my time
the smith has let the chain loose I shake my head feel
a line cool as steel trace the links my neck is free
it is the time I stalk through trees hills glens I will
kill the foes of the king I will hunt those who fear
him I will heat my fangs in the tripes of his friends
if I meet them I come in the dun dusk the dull glow
of my eyes white glint of teeth the last thing they see
they hear the suck of wet lips hot kiss at the throat
salt and sweet from torn skin I am the hound Brown
                                                    Mouse

only he can come near me I let him scratch let him
stroke I bare my teeth I do not fear him I have
no understanding I go as he lets me return as he tells me

a thing that smells good that sounds small that looks frail
juices black of my lips thin red kink of my tongue
a whelp who will cry and run as I howl I'll let him
think he escapes my appetite has no pity
I will toss him click my teeth in the air by his ear
the sweet pink of his cock the blue vein of his neck
his squeals in my ears till I swallow

before I see meat when the panic stench reeks
sweet and squeaks and scuffles tell me which hillside
which thicket I will meet my kill I howl a hoarse
and lonesome warning that spirals widdershins
to spin around the space inside their heads truer
than thin wails of the *bean sidhe* I sing the death I bring

this small boy walks to meet me huge and skulking
shadows at my shoulder the drip of spit the grunts
and growls the scrape of my claws this is a thing
I never saw before he does not run his eyes
are a suckling pup's the milk he reeks of is blood
but he is not like me he will kill without hunger
pleasure or pity only his curiosity summons death
the crackle of ribs the hand to crush my heart
tonight I am glad I will not have the world to share
with him I crouch to spring he smiles

SOLWAY

Evening will come
They will sew the blue sail
Ian Hamilton Finlay

The folding layers of rock will crack
one day while waves will still
be pulled in patterned
repetitions under moon

and wind. Feathering strata
slip inland. Leaving hills
and clouds, spilled sunlight
climbs into night, makes

the blue mask
dissolving between
us and Vega, Sirius,
Orion. First lights

on the firth; the distance
between each boat, each
point, each human
presence grows. Horizon

looks straight; a tense
bowstring. Two tips
of rock at east and west
hold it

or it holds them.

Angus Dunn

A HARD PLACE

After school we would play on the seaweedy beams under the pier. Neither of us could swim, but we never fell in. Or we would go to your house the long way, up and through the moors. Other times, we explored the old gun emplacements near the beach, each concrete shelter full of rusty barbed wire and water. In Spring, frogspawn covered the surface. Later you showed me how to cut the tails off the tadpoles, to help them turn into frogs. They couldn't swim when you dropped them back in the water.

It was the summer holidays, I remember. We turned off the road at the Manse, down onto the round-stone beach. The shoreline curved back, and round the bend was the gravel quarry, where a well-thrown rock could dislodge large slabs of gravel cliff. Or was that later? Perhaps the hillside was still rough pasture then.

On Saturday mornings I was happy to dawdle through the crofts to your house. You were always in bed. While I waited, your mother gave me tea and toast, as if I was another adult in her house. The tea was sweet, the toast thick with butter. Even today, when I put bread in the toaster, when I fill the teapot, I am trying to make that same tea, that toast.

Anyway, the sun shone brightly that day, from a wide, wide sky: the sea was liquid blue. A tractor moved slowly up and down a field on the far side of the loch, too far away to hear.

Once round the long bend of the beach, the shore became rocky and the cliffs began to encroach on the shore. At this point we usually turned up the hill, where the cliffs were easier to climb; smaller too, and there was thick heather at the base to break a fall.

When I got a rod for my birthday, I spent hours getting the line tangled in the willows and the water-weeds.

Then you came along and caught six fish with my new rod. I went home empty-handed.

But on this particular day, the tide was on the way out, so we carried on along the beach. Below the cliffs was a good place; here caves might hide Bonnie Prince Charlie's treasure, or human bones. We hunted for crabs, we fought battles. I tried to dislodge you from a fortress of rock. The day was endless. We went far beyond the furthest headland that we'd reached before. Our sandshoes got wet dancing back from the waves, clothes and skin were rubbed thin on rock scrambles.

We cycled all the way to Gruinard Bay once. My bike had a basket, so I collected the empty bottles the tourists had left behind. You lit a fire on the sand.

On the way home we ate the chocolate I bought with the bottles, and invented unlikely excuses for being late home.

It was the summer holidays. No-one had noticed we were gone.

I found the pool and called you over. It was beautiful. Most rock pools are only a foot or two deep, but this was huge, five feet deep and ten feet across. Sandshoes came off, and we sat at the edge, splashing. It was a magical place. We both grew silent. I was fascinated by the water, so clear it was barely there except for the slight shimmer of sunlight and the giveaway waving of sea anemones and small water creatures.

In the field behind your house, we began to dig a hole to Australia. The spade was too big for me, awkward to handle. We never finished it.

Years later, and I am a different person. I still dream sometimes that there is a secret cave behind the bush where we dug.

The rocks were warm, and the sun was hot. In the pool, the shimmering of the water was hypnotic. We both wanted to go in, but neither of us was sure how safe it was. As we talked about it, the sun grew hotter. The water looked more and more enticing, but the pool was deep and wide, and the sides were steep.

'If you pushed off hard from this side you'd just sort of glide across to the other side, where it's shallow.'

'Yeah, that would be great. I bet we could do that easy.'

'You wouldn't even have to be able to swim. You could just float across.'

'Aye, people are lighter than water, aren't they?'

'Anyway, your toes would probably reach the bottom.'

Then I noticed something strange. I was talking about whether we should do it. You were talking about whether I should do it.

I fell quiet, and looked at the pool. It was deeper than my height.

'Go on you can do it.'

I looked up. Your eyes were eager.

'Go on.'

For no reason that I could think of, I remembered the look on your face when you cut the tadpole's tail off.

I said no.

Colin Dunning

JUDGE NOT

```
Y  E  S
E  S  Y
S  Y  E
A  E  S
E  S  A
S  A  E
A  Y  S
Y  S  A
S  A  Y
A  Y  E
```

Dedicated to the Sheriff who sent down for
contempt a Defendant who answered 'Aye'
to the questions he was asked, telling him
to use the 'Queen's English' in his Court.

POLITICAL TRANSFORMER

```
S  C O T T  I  S  H
C  O T T  I  S  H  S
O  T T  I  S  H  S  C
T  T  I  S  H  S  C  O
T  I  S  H  S  C  O  T
I  S  H  S  C  O  T  T
S  H  S  C  O  T  T  I
H  S  C  O  T  T  I  S
R  E  O  T  T  I  S  H
E  O  T  T  I  S  H  R
O  T  T  I  S  H  R  E
T  T  I  S  H  R  E  O
T  I  S  H  R  E  O  T
I  S  H  R  E  O  T  T
S  H  R  E  O  T  T  I
H  R  E  O  T  T  I  S
R  E  P  U  T  I  S  H
E  P  U  T  I  S  H  R
P  U  T  I  S  H  R  E
U  T  I  S  H  R  E  P
T  I  S  H  R  E  P  U
I  S  H  R  E  P  U  T
S  H  R  E  P  U  T  I
H  R  E  P  U  T  I  S
R  E  P  U  B  L  S  H
E  P  U  B  L  S  H  R
P  U  B  L  S  H  R  E
U  B  L  S  H  R  E  P
B  L  S  H  R  E  P  U
L  S  H  R  E  P  U  B
S  H  R  E  P  U  B  L
H  R  E  P  U  B  L  I
R  E  P  U  B  L  I  C
```

```
S   I  L  E  N  C      E
I   L  E  N  C  E      S
L   E  N  C  E  S      I
E   N  C  E  S  I      L
N   C  E  S  I  L      E
C   E  S  I  L  E      N
E   S  I  L  E  N      C
W   H  L  E  N  C      E
H   L  E  N  C  E      W
L   E  N  C  E  W      H
E   N  C  E  W  H      L
N   C  E  W  H  L      E
C   E  W  H  L  E      N
E   W  H  L  E  N      C
W   H  E  E  N  C      E
H   E  E  N  C  E      W
E   E  N  C  E  W      H
E   N  C  E  W  H      E
N   C  E  W  H  E      E
C   E  W  H  E  E      N
E   W  H  E  E  N      C
W   H  E  E  S  H      E
H   E  E  S  H  E      W
E   E  S  H  E  W      H
E   S  H  E  W  H      E
S   H  E  W  H  E      E
H   E  W  H  E  E      S
E   W  H  E  E  S      H
W   H  E  E  S  H      T
```

Margaret Elphinstone

SILVER AND GOLD

I was right vexed with myself after she'd gone. I reckoned maybe I should of said more, maybe less. I didn't like to lie to her. I had a boy too once and I don't know what become of him neither. But I couldn't tell the whole truth, now could I? You knows that and I knows that. But I still don't feel right in my mind about how I dealt with her.

I been that busy since Jack left. I put 'The Spyglass' up for sale three days after they sailed, and that many folk've been round looking. Half of them ain't buyers. You knows that and I knows that. But you can't say no, now can you? You sees a fellow in an old frieze coat and you thinks 'no money to be got there', but you shows him round just the same, because you knows and I knows there's them in this city as has made their pile and don't want no word said about it. And a snug business like ourn, right down on the docks where you can see every ship as sails, and all that goes on the length of Bristol dock – why, isn't that just the spot as would suit the kind of gentleman I mentions? Isn't that just why Jack picked this tavern in the first place, and when he comes back to our lodging and says what the property is, don't I say, 'Very well Jack, you and I'll go down there now this minute, and if I thinks what you thinks, we'll give the man our pledge this very day.' And that's what we did, and got a receipt from him on the spot, because I ain't no flat when it comes to business, though Jack can be too casual-like, if it's a matter of words on paper. But that's where it counts – I knows that and you knows that – that's where it counts: words on paper and the gentleman's signature in his own hand on the bottom. Ain't I got my manumission like that, in that there strongbox with the lease and other docu-ments as I won't mention here. Ain't I got all that and all legal and above board, and ain't that all us has against our old age?

Treasure, says you? I don't hold with none of that. A fool's errand, that's what I says to Jack, the day Black Dog comes back in here stirring up trouble that's better let lie. Ain't they lain long enough, trouble and treasure together? Let them lie, says I. We got two thousand and then some in a safer place nor that, and what more would we be wanting? It's not as if you're a whole man, Jack, I says to him – I don't like to mention that much, but men is all alike fools when you come down to it, and some things I just has to say, though there's other times I've kept my tongue atween my teeth and been glad I done it.

After Flint got his we took our pile and got out and that was that, far as I could see. Jack's fifty now, and I reckon he has the advantage of me, though I don't have no year to count from so I can't be sure. We got neither chick nor child nor no debts neither. And when he got the gold, and that was ten years back or more, why then I took charge of it, didn't I, because I'd got Jack's measure by then. He's been a good man to me, none better, but short of common sense, as they mostly are I reckon. I had our gold safe invested in the Funds before you could say Jack Robinson, and there it's lain ever since, with the whole law and constitution keeping guard over it. It makes me laugh, that does. But we made our pile, and I'd more sense not to bury it, nor draw maps and cause trouble over it, not like Flint with all his nonsense. And hasn't it grown more each year since the day I put it there, which is better'n dumping it in a hole in the ground, where it can't do nothing for you, no more than what a dead man could? Han't we lived right well on the interest from it ever since, and each year put a bit more back?

You can't do better nor the Funds, says I. First man I went to, asking advice like, he were a cove Jack knew, who'd sold goods for gentlemen in the trade now and then. A fence you'd say if you weren't being too polite. Well, I goes to him and I says, 'I've a bit put by like and I wants it where it's safe and where it'll grow. Has you any ideas about that?' He were a cozening kind of fellow with a face like half a lemon squeezed dry and left in the back of the larder. He talks to me about Risks and Securities, and Rates of Interest, trying to bamboozle me with words what he thinks I won't understand. He han't got my measure, no sir. He says he knows of a snug little enterprise, new like: silver mines, he says. Silver mines in Venezuela. Not on the open market yet, but he'll give me the chance he says. Some chance. I tells him what I thinks and I'm out of there like the shot out of a musket, and he ain't left looking too happy about it neither.

So then I goes to this lawyer-like fellow what has a brass plate and an office what looks like it's been there forever and won't be gone tomorrow like the dew off the grass. 'This looks better' thinks I, but no sir. This cove talks to me about Golden Opportunities, and Colonial Investment. 'Don't you talk to me about no colonial investments,' says I to him. 'That's another word for a trade what I don't hold with, as you'd recognise right off if you just looked at me with half an eye.' He looks like I'd called his mother a whore, and says too quick, 'No, no, dear lady, you quite misunderstand me. I'm not speaking of that infamous trade at all. I'm a dissenting man' – he says to me – 'and I don't hold with none o' that' – or words to that effect. And him a Bristol lawyer, telling me he don't have to do with the West Coast trade, like I'd never cut my eye teeth, which I done years ago, afore I got to Trinidad even.

He talks to me about South Seas investments, but I heard all that afore. Han't I seen men begging in the streets what rode in their own coaches afore that same bubble burst the last time? So I says no to that. 'And ain't I heard' I says to him, 'about what happened to the last lot they sent out that-a-way. Ain't I heard they sunk their money and they went off to a place called Darien, before you or I was born this was, and ain't they all dead of fever, every man of 'em, and worse still, there weren't an investor what saw a farthing of his money back?' 'Ah well,' he says, 'but times have changed and they was Scotchmen what did that deal, and in this country we'd do it better.' Which was maybe true from what I've heard, for they do say them Scotchmen is just a tribe of nasty murthering heathen savages when they're at home, though mind you, we get a good few of 'em down here these days, now our markets is open to them to make free with like they was one of us, and in Bristol they're no worse than most men, which ain't saying much.

Still and all, I didn't go much by him, so then I goes to the Bank. I lines up at a high wooden counter all marred with inkstains, and the clerk looks through me like he don't see me, and the customers push past and he serve 'em one by one, and me standing there like I ain't visible to human eyes. So I reckon I've had enough of this and I shoves through and they mutters and draws their coat tails away so's not to touch my skirts as I sweep by. And I speak bold to the clerk which is a young fellow with a crop of spots and pimples on his face like I never did see afore, me being new to Bristol in them days, and my own people not being afflicted that way. I was feart he had the plague, but then I reckoned they wouldn't leave him up there on his high stool breathing affliction over well-plucked customers. So I says to him 'Young man, I've stood here half an hour while you've took no notice of me. I'll stand no more, and I'll thank you to attend to my business what I come here for.'

He glances at the men around him so's to say, 'What's this I got to deal with here,' then he leans over and says, 'So what's your business my good woman? Speak up quick for I ain't got no time to waste.' 'It's a matter of 20001,' says I, 'what I want invested tight and snug.' His jaw drops and I sees his teeth is rotten and yellow and I smell his foul breath, but I stands my ground and I says, 'And seeing as how my business is private, I'll thank you to speak to your captain, what sits in that office behind you, for ain't I seen how the swells just gets took in there right away, and no waiting about in a line like the common folk?'

So he opens the door of the gentleman's office, and I hears him say, 'Mr, — Sir, there's a fat black woman been standing out here this half hour and she won't go away nohow, not without she speaks to you sir, and what's more she says ...' And here his voice drops to a whisper and us outside don't hear no more. But the answer is favourable, and the lad with the face like a volcano the day after it went up beckons me in but he don't meet my eyes in case I puts a jinx on him, or so he reckons I guess.

So into that office I goes, and the man inside of it speaks to me like I was a lady born, for all his trade is what the Bible says a Christian man don't do. He speaks me fair, and I hand over the gold and I get his Note of Hand writ out proper, and a flourishing signature at the end of it, and a place where I makes my mark, for though I've learned to read because I don't like being cheated, I never learned writing, not even print, and on the whole I ain't had no call for it.

So that's where the money's been ever since we come ashore and it got more over the years, which is why when Black Dog come back I didn't open my arms to welcome him. I knew he'd unsettle Jack, and that vexed me. We put a lot into 'The Spyglass', Jack and me. I does the accounts and the cook-ing, and he acts landlord and buys in the drink, and we been good partners, and why would I wish for more? I never did, and that's the truth. And now Black Dog is dead and cold and don't ask me to weep for him. If you'd ever got near him you'd of seen the lice crawling over each other in his greasy hair, and that's God's truth, and whenever he'd been in I could swear we found more on ourselves afterwards. He seemed to put some kind of extra spark into them so's they could jump further, for

I'm sure I took care never to get near him, but the creatures found me just the same, and they itched more than ordinary, I do believe, though when I said so to Jack he laughed at me.

'The Spyglass' is sold now for a tidy sum, that's assuming it all comes through like it should next Monday. And I been to the Bank, and the gentleman comes out to the lobby to shake my hand, 'Mrs Silver,' says he, 'I'm glad to see you. Please walk in. And what can I do for you today?' So I sits down and waits till the door is shut, and then I says to him 'I'm selling out' and he's startled I can see, but makes no bones about it, and says he'll have the promissory note for me by Friday. 'I don't want no paper,' I says to him. 'It's real money I'm needing now. You'll need to get me gold.' He blinks a bit but he don't say nothing. I'm anxious like, waiting till he speaks. I'm thinking, 'He's putting two and two together, and he'll come up with an answer quick enough, seeing as how figures is his business. Why would I be wanting gold? says he to himself. Because I'm leaving the country, says he. Because my man is gone on a voyage all Bristol has speculated about since the day they went down channel, he says. Because I don't expect my man back here no more. Because I've a rendezvous with him, thinks he, because if Jack comes back to England they'll land him at Execution Dock, where else, and so, being a sensible man, he thinks, Jack won't come nigh the place no more.'

Well, maybe he did think all them thoughts, and maybe he didn't. Howsomever, when he'd paused for a while and scratched his head a bit so his wig sat crooked, he said, 'I think that will all be in order, madam. It will take a little while to sell your holdings, and to have the sum for you in hard currency. We can make out the order today, and perhaps you could return in a sennight?'

It were as easy as that. So there I were, back at 'The Spyglass' keeping the boy under my eye as I was rinsing out the glasses, and stirring the stew which is what we has most days for ordinary, and thinking as how the business was fairly settled, the money coming through and the tavern sold, goodwill and all, and a captain Jack knows as is willing to give me my passage to – you knows where and I knows where – but we won't speak of that out loud, not just now, because maybe that ain't lucky. But as I says, there I was, thinking as how everything's set fair and I'll be on my way in a sennight, and I'm hoping as Jack's safe and prospering on his fool's errand what I did my damnedest to

put him off of, because what's the use of all my trouble and
contriving if there ain't no Jack at the end of it? What's the use
of anything in that case? But that don't bear thinking of, and so
I don't.

Well, it seemed natural to me she should be fretted about
her boy. I'd feel the same. When she come in it took me a
moment to work out who she might be. 'Betty Hawkins
ma'am,' says she to me. 'I took the liberty and come along,
because Jim wrote as your husband be a trustworthy man,
which I were right glad to hear, because seems to me like the
whole voyage is a fool's errand from beginning to end, and I
been wishing ever since the night that Captain Bones died on us
that my boy were well out of it.'

I knew then who she must be. She were a plain pleasant-
spoken widow-woman, and I felt sorry for her, so out of place
as she were in Bristol dock, and her not knowing one thing
from another, not so much as one of them terrible Bristol
traders from an honest pirate. She weren't to know why they
build up frigates triple-decked like they do, nor how the money
come to build all them houses down Clifton way for gentry. It's
not her sort I'm blaming, though she looked at the women
eating their dinners in the tap like they was whores from
Babylon, and indeed she were right enough about the first,
though Babylon don't come into it nohow; fact was they was
good girls enough and paid their shot regular, which is the only
kind of virtue I asks of anyone.

So like I say I were sorry for her, so I sits her down and
gives her a dinner and I sits with her when things is quietened
down, and I pours her a measure and me the same, and I says,
'Don't you worry about that boy o' yours, Mrs Hawkins. I saw
him myself when he were in here, and I could see with half an
eye he were a right one. My Jack took a fancy to him, so he
did, and he'll watch over him, you may be sure, like he was his
own babby. Which same we never had, more's the pity, neither
of us being as young as we were, by the time we was wed. But
if Jack and me'd had a boy, he'd of been the spit of yours, I
reckon.' She glances at me a bit doubtful like. 'That's to say, the
half that weren't black,' says I, and she laughs a bit too shrill,
and looks away from me. But I'm working to set her at her
ease, for I can see I aint what she's used to, and like I say I'm
sorry for her and so I don't take no offence, and I tells her
again, 'Him and Jack's two of a kind, I'm telling ye. Barring

there's nigh on forty years atween 'em, I could see they were as
like as two peas out of the same pod. My Jack'll stick to your
Jim, you see if he don't.'

I'm happy to say it were the truth I telled her, so far as I
knew it. Jack HAD took a fancy to her boy. 'Smart as paint, our
Jim,' he says to me that last night. 'I don't know but what I've
taken a fancy to that boy.' 'You watch out, Jack,' says I. 'You
and your fancies. He's as thick with yon squire and doctor as
ever you were with Flint, and I don't know but what I'd trust
Flint further. It's these respectable gentry folk you don't know
where you are with. I see that Squire Trelawney when he come
in here, and I tell ye I were knocked acock, he were that like our
old Master back on the plantation. It give me the shivers just to
see him standing there in our tap like he owned the place and
all the souls inside it. That's the kind of man I don't want to
know no more about, and I'd sleep sounder in my bed if you
weren't shipped along o' him.'

But I weren't as worried about Jack as she were about her
boy. Though Jack talks sentimental sometimes, he'd never act
against his own interest, not when it come down to it. So
though I telled her the truth it were a lie as well, behind the
words, if you understand me, and that's why I'm not easy in
my mind about her. I don't like the thought that she should lose
her boy. The rest can walk the plank for all I care, but it's the
mother I'm sorry for. She weren't asked, were she? They takes
her boy and leaves her to get on with it.

We had a talk about that too, and I took to her. She seemed
a helpless kind of body concerning the business she'd come for,
but then we heard a crash of crockery from the kitchen, and I
had to go and deal with that good-for-nothing prentice boy
Jack left me. I'm meant to be selling on this business with all
the stock entire, but that lad's made such havoc with the crocks
I was fair shamed when I had to cozen the lawyer's clerk into
counting everything twice over. So that led her and me to talk
of prentices, and how a man – or a boy – might sail away and
leave you with a pauper idiot still wet behind the ears, and
think you'd hardly notice the difference from having your own
man. We spoke about Selfishness, and Treasure, and What
Fools Men Be, and time went by most pleasantly till it were
almost dusk.

So off she went, not so sore at heart as when she come. I
never asked her back, but I reckon she'll come in August, when

the Hispaniola ain't been heard of again, and it's time for the consort to set out. That's what bothers me, see. She'll come back here to 'The Spyglass', like a tired-out schooner following the lights to harbour, because it's what she's familiar with, ain't it? A snug little tavern like her own, and a woman like herself waiting for her man to come home. She'll turn up, I say, and what will she find? The bird will of flown, and the treasure with it. I'll be away – I knows where and you knows where. Still and all, I'm sorry for the soul, and I've this picture in my mind I'm feart will haunt me, of her coming along Bristol dock with her bundle over her arm. She'll be gazing at every ship in the harbour, for she don't even know which a schooner is, poor thing, just hoping against hope it might be the one. And it won't be, so on she'll come, down the quay to 'The Spyglass' looking for the strange foreign lady whose man is as like her own son as one pea to another out of the same pod. But she won't find me no more.

It don't bear thinking on, and so I won't. I got all the business done, like I say, and I'm packed and ready. He'll find me where I said I'd be, and I'll find him. I don't set my faith in no treasure – you knows that and I knows that – and it don't bother me either way. If we're not to live like gentry, we'll have another tidy inn on another quayside, in a place where the sun shines a good bit more than it do here. It'll be a good spot for folk like us; there's more of our kind there, more with stories like ours that don't bear telling here, and we'll fit in like beetles in a tree. No one won't find us no more, and that's a fact.

Colin Ferguson

A SINGULAR EXPOSURE

February 13th was no ordinary day. It was the day that the strength of my willpower was to be tested to the limit. I was determined not to fail again. My preparations had gone well. I was ready for the new challenge. That was the theory at least. The reality proved to be very different.

I entered the room and looked about me, searching for a friendly figure I could latch on to. There was a buzz of easy conversation and laughter. A few, half-familiar faces nodded in my direction. I drifted nervously around on the fringes of the group, anxious for the formal proceedings to begin.

They began much as I expected. The Chairman said a few words of welcome and then introduced me to the gathering. The room stilled to an expectant silence. I sat uneasily in my chair, conscious that all eyes were focused upon me. Everyone was waiting for me to start, to say something enlightening, perhaps, which might make them laugh or warm towards me; to provide an opening which was original and would capture their interest immediately. This was the moment of challenge I had prepared for. Now that it had arrived, the old fears surged up and were about to overwhelm me.

I could hear and feel the thumping of my heart. My swollen tongue stuck to the roof of my mouth; my lips were cracked and fiery. I gagged on the lump growing in my throat. Water. I must have water. They could wait for a few more seconds. The glass lay in front of me, a full jug by its side. It would help to steady my nerves, to focus my mind on what I had to say.

I made to reach for the glass. Nothing happened. My right hand stayed where it was on the polished surface of the table. Paralysed. I was paralysed. Surely, it wasn't possible. It doesn't happen as easily as that. I dismissed this first, crazy thought from my head and pulled. Still, nothing happened. Then without warning, my hand shot from the table in a wild, flailing motion and swatted a hundred, unseen flies in its frantic attack.

I looked up for the first time to face the expectant watchers opposite. Their faces displayed a mixture of emotions and expressions ranging from wide-eyed stares to puzzled but sympathetic smiles. They had certainly witnessed an original and unexpected opening; and one which had also taken me by surprise.

Sweat dripped from the hand held up for everyone to see. But it was no ordinary sweat; it was a sticky, white substance – like Copydex. I rubbed my fingers together. The flesh began to lift from the bones. First from the fingers, then from the back of my hand. It began to fall away from my palms. Not in pieces, but in one great, rubbery glove. The looseness spread up my arm and I was able, with my left hand, to roll it back and forth like an oversize wet-suit.

I suddenly became aware of the total silence in the room. My audience were now staring open-mouthed at the crazy show unfolding in front of them. I laughed out loud. Now that I had started, I was losing my fear of what they might think.

'Look at this,' I yelled. 'Flobble obble bloop!' I pulled the loose covering away from my hand and arm and let it slobber noisily back into place.

I was enjoying myself now – past caring. The original purpose of my presence was no longer important. I was discovering a hidden talent that I hadn't suspected in myself. How much further could I go? It was a time for self-discovery, as well as providing entertainment for the others.

I repeated the process with my left hand and arm. It was even easier the second time. With another, manic laugh, I let both arms flap and flop around in front of me. 'Flibble, flobble. Bloop, bloop,' I shouted. The fleshy mass swished back and forth in an uneven, tidal flow. With a shrug of my shoulders, I set ever increasing ripples in motion down my back and spreading forward until my stomach bounced freely on the edge of the table. Great waves came flowing back to crash onto my chin and bury my face. The feeling of freedom, of release from the tension which had come before couldn't have been greater. I had never felt such ecstasy.

The attention of the others was firmly fixed upon me. Some smiled in support, others nodded. They were proving to be a good and responsive audience. They deserved more.

I jumped from my seat, the loose upper half of my body squelching loudly as it flowed from side to side. From the waist down, there was still no unusual movement. I clambered up on to the table top. For an instant, panic showed on the faces of those nearest to me. They slipped their chairs quickly back, anxious not to become too closely enveloped in the action.

With an Elvis-like thrust of my pelvis and a sudden wiggle of my hips, I set my whole body in motion. 'Yippee – floppa,

loppa loo!' I roared. A mountain of loose, pink flesh piled up on the table. I stretched down and grabbed the layers of blanc-mange gathered at my ankles and hauled them up as far as they would go.

'Are you ready? Are you flopping ready?' I demanded.

'Yes,' they shouted. 'Flop away – flop away!'

I was elated with their response. They were totally with me now. It was time for something extra special – more control, more rhythm in the action. The pace needed to be built up. Their attention mustn't be allowed to wander.

I released the layers gathered up on my right side and sent a concertina pattern flowing up and down my leg from ankle to thigh. As the first wave broke at my right ankle, I set my left side moving. As one side swashed upwards, the other swished downwards. 'Swish, swash. Swish, swash'. The sound built up as the flow increased. The table was an amplifier, sending the sounds of the sea echoing round the room and engulfing the audience. The alternating wave pattern had them entranced.

But I had to change the tempo for one last time, to build towards a dramatic finale. Something extraordinary was called for. I concentrated hard, focusing my attention on building up the pressure, on increasing the power. They had witnessed breakers running up the beach. Now it was time for storm waves to crash against the cliffs.

I could feel them urging me on. They rocked back and forward in their seats. The chair legs beat a rhythmic pounding on the wooden floor. The tempo was frantic. They were now a vital and integral part of the performance. Their continued participation was essential if I was to succeed. The moment had arrived. The conditions were perfect. I had to go for it.

I screamed at the top of my voice. 'Flobble, wobble. Flobble, wobble. Double wobble. Double wobble. Wobble, wobble, wobble...' Faster and faster I shouted. Faster and faster they rocked. They chanted loudly, in unison with me. 'Flobble, wobble! Flobble, wobble! Double wobble, flobble wobble wobble! Double flobble wobble – wooooooo!'

A tidal wave of flesh crashed down on to the table and then in an overwhelming backwash shot straight back over my head and attached itself to the ceiling. I was left, a mere skeleton, exposed for all to see, without the comforting camouflage of my public persona. I looked up to where my fatty remains hovered in suspended animation like a giant, quivering, strawberry jelly.

Below me, the sea of faces looked on, stunned into a deathly silence. They no longer rocked in their seats, but sat transfixed by the spectacular climax. Entranced or shocked, it was difficult to tell. But they, like me, had certainly experienced something out of the ordinary. We looked momentarily at each other, wondering what would happen next. Then, with one enormous slurp, my flesh fell away from the ceiling.

'Bloop – bloop' it sounded as it sunk back into place and drowned my bones. The sudden weight knocked me off my feet and with one final shout of 'Flobble, obble' I fell backwards into my seat.

All around me was the sound of applause. A satisfied smile spread across my face as I realised that I had achieved my aim. I lowered my head and let out a sigh of relief. The words of congratulations came from all directions to confirm that it had been worth all the agony and effort.

The Chairman got to his feet. 'It is never easy for someone to perform before us for the first time. I know that Alan was fearful that he might find the whole experience too intimidating for him. But, having resolved to address us, he persevered and to great effect. He poured so much of himself into his speech, we could not be other than totally engrossed and entertained by his efforts. Well done, Alan. I have great pleasure in welcoming you now as a fully fledged member of our Speakers' Club.'

Paul Finn

CLACH DHUBH SPEUR DUBH

am balla an uinneag
fosgailte

t'aghaidh 'san oidhche
dubh

dubh air son fola
dubh air sgàth fola
      air sgàth doirteadh fola

dubh is duibhead falaichte fo luaithre
aghaidh no uilebheist
      amar
dubh is ruadh na h-aibhne dubh is craobh-dhearg

sgrìobhte gun bhreugriochd
      is mar sgaoil
clach dhubh, speur dubh
an so: gniomh a dhearbhadh anns an fhògradh
m' fhianais earbsach.

BLACK STONE BLACK SKY

the wall the window
open

your face in the night
black

black for blood
black for the sake of blood
        for the sake of shedding blood

black and blackness hidden beneath ashes
face or monster
        the bed of a river
black and ochre black and crimson

written without disguise
            as
black stone black sky
have spread here: an act of affirmation in exile
my faithful witness.

Pete Fortune

IN AN AGE OF ADVANCED COMMUNICATIONS

'Have you seen Kelvin's number anywhere?' he called.

'Kelvin who?' she replied.

'Kelvin Bridge from *Rabble Think*. I was supposed to phone him about the venue for the reading tomorrow night. Star turn and I still don't know where I'm supposed to be performing. I definitely left his number in the book here.'

'Well I haven't moved anything.'

'Are you sure? It was on a sheet of green paper.'

'Yes, my dear husband, I'm sure.'

'Bloody hell, where's it got to then?'

'There's always directory enquiries,' she said.

'I don't know his address,' he replied. 'There's just a PO Box printed in *Rabble Think*, and there's bound to be loads of K. Bridge's in the Edinburgh area. Listen, Vlad will have his number. I remember him saying he'd had to phone Kelvin about something one time. Phone him for me, will you? You said you've been meaning to phone him anyway. Don't spend half the day yapping though.'

'Vlad's out, but I left a message.'

'Typical. Who else is there? I know – Angus Anxious. He's a pal of Kelvin's. He's *bound* to have his number. Polygone John will have Angus Anxious' number. Phone old Jake for me, will you?'

'And where exactly does Jake fit into the equation?' she asked.

'He'll have Polygone John's number. I've got it upstairs somewhere but it'll take forever to find.'

'Unpaid secretary,' she said.

'Go on, phone old Jake for me. You'll have to shout mind.'

'He doesn't have it but he gave me Stoat's number. Says he should have Polygone John's number. I suppose you want me to phone *him* now?'

'Good gal. You might have to shout at him too, mind.'

'I got the number. Apparently Polygone John lives in some kind of boarding house now, so anyone's liable to answer the phone. Stoat made it sound like some sort of doss house.'

'*Doss House?* Christ, he must be skint. Right enough, mind he was going on about selling someone a half share in his car?'

'That's right,' she replied, 'it was an old banger too.'

'Ancient old thing,' he said. 'He was trying to rent it out for car boot sales. Jesus, times must be hard. Imagine a critically-acclaimed novelist having to live in a doss house.'

'I didn't say it *was* a doss house,' she cautioned, 'it was just the way Stoat said anyone was liable to answer. The sort of image it conjured up. It could be a respectable B+B for all you know. And besides, Stoat said he has a notion he might be in Italy.'

'Who might be in Italy?'

'Polygone John.'

'Ha! Can't be that skint after all then. Maybe I should think about writing full time.'

'Maybe you should,' she replied, 'better than the dole.'

'Give me the bloody number,' he said.

'Polygone John's not in,' he said. 'It was some woman who answered the phone. I don't know whether he's in Italy or not. I asked but she became kind of flustered so I just hung up. She sounded a bit simple to tell you the truth. God knows what sort of place he's got himself holed up in.'

'I came across this,' she was saying, 'in the wee black phone book. Is it Kelvin Bridge's number? It's certainly an Edinburgh number and it's your writing.'

'I doubt it,' he replied, 'I doubt it, but I'll give it a go anyway.'

'Nothing. Just a continuous tone. Whatever it was, it can't be a legitimate number any more. I'm telling you, Kelvin's number was written on *green* paper. It made me think of Shoogly McHooligan.'

'Why did it make you think of Shoogly McHooligan?'

'Because he's a Hibs fan. So's Kelvin Bridge, come to think of it. Ha! Remember that poem I had in *Best Boast Magazine* about Easter Road? Can't have been many poems written about the old Hi-Bees, eh? I bet Peter Marinello doesn't know he featured in a poem published in *Best Boast Magazine*.'

'Maybe they cut him off,' she suggested.

'Who's cut who off?'

'Telecom,' she replied. 'Maybe they cut Kelvin off. Another impoverished writer.'

'It's a tough business,' he replied, 'but it wasn't Kelvin's number. Green, I'm telling you, *green* paper. I know! I'll phone Bunker McBane. He's a big pal of Kelvin's, he's bound to have his number. I've got his new address in Orkney.'

'Orkney?'

'Yes,' he replied, 'he moved to Orkney. If I'd taken that residency in Shetland we could have bawled across the water at each other.'

'I thought Bunker McBane was a janitor at some school in Edinburgh?' she said.

'Something like that, I'm not too sure, but anyway he moved to Orkney. Picked up the *Somerset Maugham* award, you know. That was showing the buggers, eh? I think he *was* a jannie at some school, you know. I think you're right. Ha! I wonder how he got on with the English teachers? Maybe they spent their free periods in the boiler room, gathered in a wee circle at Bunker's feet.'

'I got his number, but there's no reply.'

'Whose number?' she wanted to know.

'Bunker bloody McBane's.'

'What about Iggy Burroughs?' she suggested.

'What about Iggy Burroughs?'

'Well, his stuff's always in *Rabble Think* isn't it?'

'Yes, but I don't have his number.'

'Directory enquiries,' she suggested.

'Fifty pence a go though. Can't afford to run up too many of those.'

'It'll hardly break the bank,' she replied.

'Go on then,' he said, 'phone directory enquiries for me.'

'Apparently three Iggy Burroughs, but one ex-directory.'

'Have you got the other two numbers?' he asked.

'Yes.'

'Iggy Burroughs, eh? Give me them here, quick.'

'Hello, can I speak to Iggy please? Oh I see, I'm sorry.'

'Hello, can I speak to Iggy please? Oh I see, I'm sorry.'

'Elitist bastard, eh? What a turncoat. Bloody ex-directory indeed.'

'So would I be if I thought the likes of you were liable to phone and pester me.'

'Hang about,' he said, 'didn't someone say he'd moved to Amsterdam?'

'Amsterdam?'

'Yes, now I think about it I'm sure Shoogly McHooligan said Iggy Burroughs had moved to Amsterdam.'

'Why does he want to move to Amsterdam?'

'Why do you think Iggy Burroughs wants to move to Amsterdam?'

'The phone!' she called. 'I'll let you get it.'

'Hello? Oh hello Vlad, how are you? Good holiday? Good, glad to hear it, man. Tell you what it is Vlad. I'm trying to get in touch with Kelvin at *Rabble Think* and wondered if you had his number. I see. Right. Yes? Angus Anxious' number? Brilliant. Yes, I'm sure he will. Thanks Vlad. I've got that, great. Eh? Oh the *Writers Register*. The copy I have is ancient. Got folk like MacDiarmid in it. He's never at home though. Ay, Burns too. Ha! Who'd want Rabbie Burns on the phone to them, eh? Just be phoning to see if you were out so he could pop round and shag your wife. Ha! Eh? Ay, she's here. Bye now. Ann! It's Vlad. Says he wants a quick word.'

'You were an eternity,' he said, 'yap yap all day. Glad it was *his* phone bill. God knows what you two find to yap about.'

'He was asking if you had a job yet.'

'Give me the phone, he gave me Angus Anxious' number.'

'Did you get him?' she asked.

'No. It wasn't Angus Anxious' number, not quite. It was... oh never mind, it's kind of complicated.'

'What are you going to do now then?'

'I haven't a bloody clue,' he replied. 'Maybe broadcast an appeal on radio.'

'The only radio you're ever on is *West Sound*,' she said, 'and I doubt if Kelvin Bridge listens to *West Sound*. In fact, I hardly know anyone who listens to *West Sound*.'

'Hang about,' he said, taking off upstairs.

'What's that you've got?' she asked.

'An old *Rabble Think* reject slip. There's a phone number on it. The number for enquiries about advertising it says. That's a laugh. Who ever advertises in *Rabble Think*? I'll give it a go anyway.'

'Well?'

'Some guy called Brando. Doesn't have Kelvin's number as such, but he gave me a number to try. He seemed a bit vague, maybe even suspicious. I told him I was on a literary tour of Scotland by telephone. He said I couldn't be *that* literary because I wasn't watching Coronation Street. Sarcastic bastard. I don't think he'd even heard of me, you know. Anyway, I'll give it a go. What a bloody carry-on this is.'

'I don't believe it,' he said. 'That *continuous* tone again. What is it with all these Edinburgh numbers? Maybe they've dropped an atomic bomb on the place.'

'You wouldn't have to worry about the reading then,' she said.

'I'm not worrying about the reading. I'm worrying about not *getting* to the reading.'

'What about Flora Gardens?'

'What about Flora Gardens?' he repeated.

'Well she lives in Edinburgh, doesn't she? Won't she have Kelvin's number?'

'Doubtful,' he replied. 'Besides, I can't very well phone Flora Gardens, can I? Not after the last time. Prickly issue that one, isn't it?'

'Oh yes, of course. You bloody idiot.'

'Who you been trying now?' she wanted to know.

'I keep trying Bunker McBane's number, but there's no answer. Maybe he's popped out to see Jaws McAye Broon.'

'Who's Jaws McAye Broon?'

'Who's Jaws McAye Broon? Shame on you woman. He's one of the old masters, looks like a kind of wild Jimmy Hill, but without the beard.'

'Anyway,' she said, 'what you going to do now?'

'Don't know. Blackface Hodgson maybe. I bet he'll have Kelvin's number, or at least know the venue.'

'Where does he live?'

'Cloud-cuckoo land.'

'Eh?'

'The town of Hair. They say he lives with a flock of sheep you know. Anyway, I'll maybe look up his number at the library tomorrow. Save myself fifty pence.'

'Listen,' she said. 'What's that?'

'What's what?'

'Listen. There's music coming from somewhere. What a racket.'

'Across the road,' he said. 'That guy's doing Paterson's garden again. Always has to have the radio blaring. Listen, Val Doonican isn't it?'

'Elvis, you fool.'

'So it is. Imagine confusing Elvis with Val Doonican. Ha! Can you see Elvis done out in one of those big daft jerseys? Funny enough, I was looking through the wee black phone book earlier on and I thought I saw Val Doonican's number in it, but it wasn't.'

'You don't say.'

'But that must be why I thought it was Val Doonican on the radio there. A kind of auto-suggestion, you see? Val Doonican's been working on me subliminally.'

'You would maybe spot Vlad's number in the book and mistake it for Val Doonican,' she said. 'You know, think Vlad was Val.'

'It was some other Val, actually. Val Donaldson I think.'

'Val Donaldson?' she repeated. 'I was at college with her. Shows you how old *that* book is. She was an Elvis fan, come to think of it.'

'Talking of Elvis,' he said, 'do you remember Jim Barbour, the funny guy who lived near us in the old house? He'd a dog called Elvis.'

'That's right,' she replied. 'Remember it got lost and Barbour roamed the scheme shouting on it?'

'Christ, that's right. Just after Elvis Presley died and Barbour was trailing the streets in the middle of the night, bawling "Elvis! Where are you?"'

'The phone!' she called. 'I'll let you get it.'

'Wrong number. Somebody wanting a taxi would you believe?'

'Could have been a nice little earner,' she said. 'Pity we don't have the car anymore.'

'Christ, you'd think it easy enough laying your hands on someone's phone number. So much for the revolution in information technology, eh?'

'You've no idea at all of the venue?'

'Edinburgh, that's all. Suppose it's a start, eh?'

'You could just turn up in Edinburgh and ask someone.'

'Do me a favour, woman.'

'Relax will you?'

'*Relax?* This is serious. I'd better phone Shoogly and explain the situation. He's supposed to be giving me a lift up. In the car, like.'

'Well, I kind of gathered that. I didn't think he'd be carrying you there.'

'Not in,' he said. 'Away fishing apparently. Bloody marvellous, eh? He's relaxing by some river bank while I'm here busting a gut and running up a massive phone bill.'

'Was it Jo who answered?'

'No. I think she's off fishing too. Some friend answered. That's what she said. *I'm a friend.* They never seem to leave the house without having a friend occupy the place. They must be kind of neurotic.'

'The kids,' she was saying, 'that's why there will be a friend there. Do you expect them just to abandon the kids?'

'It's a thought. Bet it was our bloody kids who moved Kelvin's number in the first place. If it wasn't for them I wouldn't be in this mess.'

'You're always going on about how many folk you know on the Scotlit scene.'

'*Meaning?*'

'Well, someone must know how to get in touch with Kelvin Bridge.'

'Yes,' he replied, 'Bunker McBane, and he's busy supping beer with old Jaws McAye Broon. Iggy Burroughs is either ex-directory now he's famous, or maybe he's out vein-spotting in Amsterdam. And Edinburgh, it would seem, has been destroyed by an atomic bomb. I'm sure that Brando guy had Kelvin's number you know, but was just being fucking cagey.'

'Well, if you'd put the number somewhere safe in the first place.'

'I *did* put it somewhere safe. Fuck it, I can remember distinctly. Bet it was you when you were tidying up.'

'I never laid a finger on it,' she protested.

'The bloody kids then. Shit. This is an absolute tragedy you know. My big chance and now it's all in ruins. I'm going to have a whisky. A pint of the stuff, then I'm going to... the phone! I'll get it.'

'Kelvin. Bloody hell. *!!KELVIN!!* Fuck me fucking rigid, Kelvin! You've no idea. The hassle. WOW! Kelvin Bridge. Kelvin my ultimate soul mate. Yes, same here man. WOW! Brando? Marlon Brando? Yes, that's right. Just a wee while ago actually. What? You're joking. Last night? Really? It was last night? That's a shit. How the fucking hell did I... you're not winding me up? No. No, that's okay, man. No sweat. Sure. Some other time. Ha! Can't be helped man. What a shit, eh? Bloody hell. No, no it's... yes, some other time. Sure. Hear from you man. Take care. Yes. No big deal. Bye Kelvin.'

'That was Kelvin. Kelvin Bridge. Apparently it was... take that grin off your face woman. Pour me a drink. Whisky. Fill a bucket. What do you mean it's finished? Beer? Oh forget it. Where's my jacket? Eh? Out. I'm off out... eh?... where?... not fucking well fishing, that's for sure. See you. I'll maybe phone. I'll phone if I'm going to be... oh forget it.'

Paul Foy

BEDROOM SWIMMING

The curtains open and she heads off, but we don't wave or shout cheerio even though we feel that perhaps we should; some of the people here might think it inappropriate. It's a delicate situation for those who didn't know her as well as we did. So instead we've hired a man who never knew her to say some words about how she was a lovely person and everybody who knew her, even if only giving her her pension money over a counter, liked her. All true of course, but what does the minister know about the video or bedroom swimming?

I would never be able to look after myself. I didn't know how to hoover or work the washing machine. While we lived in the same house we made a good team: she kept the house and my clothes clean; I switched the telly channels for her. The paradox of my being completely useless and her reliance on me to help her deal with some of the more modern technological devices was something that never occurred to her, and who was I to bring it to her attention? And anyway, she would neither know nor care what a paradox was; she could burp like nobody's business.

There were four different newspapers brought daily into our household: The Evening Times; The Daily Record; The Daily Express; and The Glasgow Herald. Everyone apart from Gran would look at all the papers, though we would question one another on our choice of purchase:

'What do you buy this rubbish for? It's just a bloody comic.'

'Well you're reading it, aren't you?'

'Look! Look at this; it's got nothing in it but soap opera gossip and tips on how to improve your sex life.'

'Well, maybe that's what people want to read. People like you, for example.'

'I'm just keeping up to date with what amuses the plebs these days.'

'You mean the real people. Unlike the pretentious gits like you that buy this tripe. It just uses big words to try and confuse folk, and people like you sit with it on the train to try and look intelligent.'

Gran's contribution to these debates was limited, but fairly regular. 'What do you buy that English muck for?' she would ask, referring to The Express, the one paper that she refused to even pick up.

'Look at the name of this paper, Gran. It's the *Scottish Daily Express*. Can't you see the word *"Scottish"* in the title?'

But Gran would not be convinced, nor would she argue; she didn't need to. She would stare contemptuously at you, narrow her eyes and drag out an ironic, 'Aaaaayyyye'. She would then return her attention to whatever she was doing and ignore us; it was what we deserved.

Whenever we came into possession of one of the newspapers that Gran had read we could never find the telly page as the pages had invariably been rearranged. I could read my preferred newspaper during the day, on the train or during my lunchbreak. But whenever we arrived home they were given to Gran and no one else got to see them until she had read – and struggled with, fought and defeated – them in their entirety. We could bicker over The Express if we wanted.

At around eight-thirty each evening the family would congregate in the living room and moan because there was nothing better on than *Eastenders*. It remained on, though, at an irritatingly loud volume. Gran liked it – or rather, liked it to be on – so that was that.

'But Gran,' we would protest, 'It's full of miserable English people just moaning and whining and generally being completely depressing.'

'It's about normal, common people and it's for normal common people,' our socialist Gran would tell us – international borders didn't matter a jot when it came to the working-class. Actually, I thought we were middle-class. For the last twenty years the family had lived in a semi-detached house in a fairly well-off suburb of Glasgow. But despite the fact that it had been through the older generation's struggles that we had ascended so high on the social ladder, there was a constant class war waging in our house – we, the young ones, were the evil Tory suppressers; the oldies the defiant salt of the earth victims. So, in the case of *Eastenders*, despite the fact that Mum and Dad hated it too, the battle lines were drawn up and the elderly ones won outright and we all had to suffer as Gran got her way.

To the sound of griping cockneys we would try and put the pages of the papers back together. Happy with the confusion she had caused Gran would get on with her knitting – 'I can knit and watch telly at the same time!' – muttering a litany of numbers which could have had something to do with the stitches she was knitting, though I suspected that she was really recounting to herself the new order of that day's pages. She was wreaking revenge for the fact that we had an advantage over her where the operation of the TV and the VCR were concerned.

The clicking of the knitting needles would often be punctuated by her farting. No one could fart and get away with it like my gran. She would be knitting away, whispering 'Forty-five, seven, nine, that makes – let me see: two,' there would be a soft but audible 'Phrrrt' and she would continue with, 'and eleven makes a hundred and five.' Papers would be lowered and noses crinkled conspiratorially, but nothing would ever be said.

She bought herself a video tape once, which was surprising because she usually not only declined but objected if any of us offered to tape a programme for her when she was feeling too worn out to stay up and watch it. 'Look Gran,' we would tell her, 'there are plenty of spare tapes we can put it on and you can watch it tomorrow sometime.' 'Och, I don't have time for watching telly,' she would shake at us, then gather up her knitting and head upstairs to bed.

One day: 'I'm going to buy a video.' It was as simple as that. Each one of us was shown in turn the advert in the paper. £12.99 it was going to cost, including postage and packaging. She already had the coupon all filled in ready to be cut out and put in the envelope which was waiting, addressed and stamped. But we all had to see it in the newspaper first. Then it was done and I was allowed to take it round to the post-box to reassure me that I wasn't completely useless.

The advert for the video was in The Daily Record. This was the paper that she spent the most time over, narrowly beating the other 'Scottish' tabloid, The Evening Times, into second place. These were the papers that dealt with, in their human interest stories, the people who were of interest to her. Life would have been hell for us if she had pored over The Glasgow Herald in detail. If making a noise with a broadsheet newspaper had been an Olympic event then my gran would have put Dougie Donelly in his place on the Scottish Sportsperson of the Year programme, though she would probably only have given the recording of it a cursory glance and a disapproving mutter. The VCR was a lifesaver for us. If you wanted to hear a programme while Gran was dealing with The Herald you had best just give up the ghost and tape it to watch later. And, of course, the VCR also came in handy for taping those programmes that we suspected might contain scenes that we deemed unsuitable for our aged relative:

'What was that play on Channel Four last night like?'

'Aye, not bad.'

'Worth watching then?'

'Yeh, I think so. Though I wouldn't watch it in front of Gran.'

We didn't like to shock the old soul.

Of course, sometimes we would get caught out. Gran would be sitting up later than usual, knitting away, while the rest of us slumped innocently and looked at the flickering in the corner. Then a change would come over the atmosphere in the room. This hadn't been expected. As the morals of the TV characters slackened, the back muscles of this particular set of viewers tightened. Shoulders were pulled back, hands rubbed necks, backs straightened. It was one of *those* programmes. We couldn't just get up and leave the room, or even change channels; that would be an admission of mortification. So we would reach for the newspapers for defence:

'Is that The Herald under the coffee table? Could you pass it over please?'

'What was that one you picked up? Could I see it a minute?'

We were fooling nobody.

Then came the big moment: the camera shots seemed to change with an unhealthy rapidity, discomfiting angles were employed and there they were in the bedroom; the music sending out bulletins as to what was taking place. Could you believe it, we were ignorant of the signals. Just at the crucial moment we all seemed to have found some article of such interest that we had to bury our heads in our papers.

'...and sixteen makes seventy-two and fourteen and seven...'

Her whispering would fade to silence and all the sounds left were those from the telly and the clicking of her knitting needles. Then the latter would stop, and though we were all staring directly in front of us, at our papers, we knew that she was looking unashamedly at our source of embarrassment.

'Tut tut tut, swimming again,' she would say and that would be it. Mostly. Sometimes she would let loose with a 'Brrrp' before returning to her incomprehensible calculations.

The video Gran ordered through the post features a concert

of Scottish fiddle music. It was the only video she ever owned, but it seemed to fit easily into the family's collection of films and somehow even managed to achieve a position of dominance. When visitors came they were made aware of my gran's purchase and it was no problem to put it on to create a background atmosphere. Create a background atmosphere for Gran's stories to be precise. If you've ever known an old person you'll know how my gran's stories went. She would go from Scottish music to her son's bagpipe playing during national service to Wee Annie Jameson who lived in the next close up across from Jeannie McClure no it was Sophie Anderson, Jeannie lived one up and on to some other event a decade or two away and with a connection that only she could see. Yet no matter how often the elderly's ramblings were parodied and made fun of they refused to become cliched; we were always left with a feeling that we had just had a glimpse into a mythical past – no matter how much we though we weren't listening.

This is how I remember my gran. I don't know if I have chosen it this way, or if this is just the way it has to be. The minister, in his brief, well-meaning speech, tried to put her life into some sort of order. Where she was born, what church she had been married in, her additions to the human race, then her additions' additions. He did a good job; better than I could have done. Had I got up to speak at her funeral service I may have started off well enough, but sooner or later I would have had to mention the video and from there to Scottish music and onwards would be but a small, simple step. I don't even know if I could ever tell anyone, face to face, about her farts and the bedroom swimming, but no matter; there's an abundance of material to choose from.

Magi Gibson

BAT SONG

So, our features offend
you. Too shrunken-
skulled, too rat-eyed.
Ugly web-winged embryos.

Skinny in leather and slinky
fur, do you find our forms
too nazi for your
civilised sensibilities?

You blame the moon
for our presence.

But we have always been/are
always here –

armies of us sleeping
in your soul-less churches,
fornicating in the rafters,
pissing on prayerbooks and pews.

Or lurking in dark dank
places your kind once too
inhabited.

We stream at dusk like smoke
into your streets, scribe
the thin black air with
strange graffiti.

You claim we make your
flesh crawl, appearing
out of darkness and silence.

Is it our fault, Sir,
that you are deaf
to the beauty of our songs?

Rody Gorman

NAM CHLARSAIR BALBH

Shil mi ceòl dhut air crann nan teud
Fo stiùireadh a' bhàird

'S gheàrr thu dhìom m' ìnean
'S thug thu an ceòl às mo mheòir

'S dh'fhàg thu mi nam amadan
Leam fhìn a' gabhail nan deòr.

ME AS A DUMB HARPER

I poured out music for you on the tree of strings
Under the bard's guidance

And you cut off my nails
And took the music out of my fingers

And left me a fool
On my own uttering tears.

NAM IAIN ODHAR

Bidh mi togail
Mo phìob' nam Iain Odhar
Ach an cuir a' ghleadhraich na cois
Mo chuimhn' ort mu làr

Ach air cho dùrachdach
'S gun sèid mi m' anail,
Bidh thu fhathast air mo chùlaibh
Nad dhos
Nach siubhail air falbh
Ach a chumas am fonn agam rèidh.

ME AS IAIN ODHAR

I lift up my pipe
Like Iain Odhar
So that the racket it makes
Will get rid of my memories of you

But however earnestly
I blow on with my breath
You'll still be there behind me
As a drone
That won't go away
But which keeps my trim/melody regular.

LOCH

Smaoinich!
Thusa nad loch
Agus reothadh cruaidh air uachdar
Anns an do shnàmh mi rùisgte uair.

LOCH

Just imagine!
You a loch
With a hard sheet of ice on its surface
In which I swam naked once.

DUBH

Cha drùidh mi ort fhèin
Ach nam dhubh
Nach tig am follais
Ach uair ainneamh nad fhianais
'S mi ri saothair
Gus d' ìomhaigh a chur an làthair
A-staigh ann am marbhan
Na duilleig' air do bheulaibh.

INK

I can only make an impression on you
As ink
Which only becomes visible
Very occasionally in your presence
As I labour
To present your image
In the margin
Of the page in front of you.

GUTH NA CHAILLICH

Tha 'n dithis againn
Nar suidhe nar suidheachain
Air beulaibh an telebhisein
'S e gun dath gun fhuaim

'S tha mise sealltainn
Air lasair an teine
'S i a' gabhail 's ag èirigh
'S a' falbh a-mach à sealladh

'S thig guth na caillich nam chuimhne
'S i coiseachd a-staigh air an doras:
– A bhalgair gun fheum!
Tha thu air a leigeil bàs!

THE CAILLEACH'S VOICE

The two of us
Are sitting in our chairs
In front of the television
Without colour or sound

And I'm watching
The flames in the fire
As they take and rise
And disappear from view

And I'm reminded of the cailleach's voice
As she walks in the door:
– You useless article!
You've let it die!

W.N. Herbert

THE BABY POEM INDUSTRY POEM

Sensitive male minus labour pains equals poem.
Production rate increases in inverse proportion
to childcare units as follows:
one couplet per five cloacal nappy non-encounters;
one stanza per non-milky-upchucked-on work shirt;
one poem per missed shift of all-nite colic alert;
one volume per year of missed meals in which
beans must be halved and omelettes rolled
into yellow trumpets, plus three hours
of night-night rituals including
march round marmite-smeared dwelling
chanting 'When-uh sains' and nine renditions
of story about haddock.

Sensitive male supplies plethora of loving
metaphors for partner including:
galactic dugong, pot-noodle of robust abundance,
shining wing-mirror extension for caravans
of completed individuation process,
symphonic Fiorentina team of
graceful scheduling and loving-kindness.
Sensitive male imagines he can see
the creation of the universe
by examining her epesiotomy scars.

Sensitive male's publisher is not impressed,
rendering the sensitive one suddenly aware
of the fact
he has not had sex
for nine months.
He casually but lyrically mentions this
in evening poem faxed home from work.
Sensitive male is suddenly aware on returning home
of unusual ice-pick adorning his forehead.

Partner commences series
of highly-profitable elegies.

GREY THRUMS

Lissen til
thi baudrins purr
hur grey thrums til
thi bairnie-o;
she's weavan thrums
intil a plaid
tae hap aboot
thi bairnie-o.

She's weavan thrums
o moosewab fur
an feathers fae
green linties-o;
she's weavan thrums
fae mawkies' fuds
an thi doon aff a
yella-yitie-o.

She's weavan thrums
oot o hur dwaums
o claain doon
a hornie ool;
she's weavan thrums
oot o hur dwaums
o grallochin
a cuddie-o.

Sae gin ye dinnae
gang tae sleep
ma pair wee skrauchan
bairnie-o,
she'll weave hur thrums
oot o yir thairms
an hap thum roon
yir thrapple-o.

Sae lissen til
thi baudrins purr
hur grey thrums til
thi bairnie-o;
she's weavan thrums
intil a plaid
tae hap aboot
thi bairnie-o.

Baudrins	cat
grey thrums	purring noise
hap	wrap
moosewab	cobweb
green lintie	greenfinch
mawkies' fuds	rabbits' tails
yella-yitie	fieldfare
hornie ool	horned owl
grallochin	eviscerating
skrauchan	screaming
thairms	intestines
thrapple	throat

THE PEARL

Once there was a man and woman who lived together in a small white house in a small green valley. They loved each other a great deal but they were unable to have children. However, they worked very hard at the things they cared about, and were very happy together. One day, the woman had to go off on a long journey because of her work, and leave the man on his own. They were upset, but they both agreed it was good for her career, and would give him time alone to get on with his own tasks.

The time came for her to go. They went for a walk to the river which ran through their valley, and stood looking at the water for a while, then returned to their home, she got in her car, and, after many protestations of love, she drove away.

For a while, all went well with the man, even though he was alone, and missed the woman very much. Summer was approaching, and the days were sunnier and sunnier. The swifts which always nested in their eaves came back, and the whole valley was full of green leaves and birdsong.

Then one night the man had a peculiar dream. He dreamt he saw a little girl trapped inside a great transparent bubble. The body of the little girl was pressed up against the wall of the bubble as though she was trying to get out, but her eyes were shut, and the bubble seemed quite rigid. Then the little girl's eyes opened, and seemed to look directly at him, and at that point he thought, 'It's a pearl; she's trapped inside a pearl.' At that point he woke up.

He found he had a terrible headache that hurt so much he could scarcely bend over. He tried taking some pills for it but it didn't go away, so he lay in bed and had a most miserable day.

The next day the pain was a little bit better, and he was able to go for a walk through the valley. The sky was a brilliant blue, almost cloudless, and there was a great deal of birdsong. Cattle came to the fences and watched him pass, and through the hedges he could hear sheep cropping at the grass. Their lambs all ran away as he went past. He thought, 'This is such a beautiful place; if only I didn't have this headache I would be able to enjoy it so much more.'

That night he dreamt of an old tobacco pouch he had never seen in waking life. It was leather, and in the shape of a horn, but with flat faces. On one face there was a metal plate engraved with a scene from a small town he was familiar with from his childhood, a seat of learning. There were figures in eighteenth-century costume going about their business in the market place, and one detail that seemed to stand out; a potato merchant who had a sign declaring him to be 'a siccar picker'.

In the dream he was turning the pouch over in his hands, opening it and playing with the lock, when he realised there was a secret compartment in the lid. Somehow he managed to click this open, and inside he found a tiny pearl. Again he woke up, and again he had a terrible headache.

By now he was growing worried, as he was usually calm and healthy, and never suffered from headaches, so he went to his doctor, who reassured him it was just tension and there was nothing to worry about. He went home feeling much relieved and his symptoms abated for a day or two. But then he had the dream of the little girl again, looking at him as if she was pleading for help to get out of the pearl. And when he awoke the headache was back.

By now he was very worried indeed, and wished he could talk to the woman, to ease his mind. But she was far away, and it wouldn't be easy to get in touch with her. In any case, it was a very important job, and he didn't want to worry her with trivialities, as that was all that was wrong with him. So he went back to the doctor.

This time the doctor was much more concerned, and booked him in to see a specialist at the hospital. He had never had to go to a hospital before for anything, so he was very afraid indeed. He walked the lanes of the beautiful valley, but found he could scarcely concentrate on the birds and the wild flowers. His mind was filled by the image of the pearl with the little girl inside it, and he wondered what it could mean.

He went down to the water where they had talked before the woman had to go away, and he looked at the flowing water for a long time, but the pain in his head would not go away.

Eventually the time came for him to go into hospital and see the specialist. The specialist put his head in a strange machine, and took photographs of the inside of it, then said he was going to have to operate and that the man had better contact the woman.

The man had never felt so alone. He sent word to the woman about what was happening, but he knew it would take too long to reach her. He felt wretched at the thought of her receiving such bad news in such a faraway place, and he also felt miserable to be spoiling her job. But he needed her very desperately.

The man was right; it took a long time for the message to reach the woman, and when it did, she was deeply shocked and very upset. She hurried home as quickly as she could, but by the time she got there the specialist had already performed the operation.

He received her in his office with a woeful face and said she must prepare herself for a terrible shock. She sat down, feeling sick, with a cold nerve of fear shooting up her spine. The news was very strange. The man had died during the operation, but that was because they had had to perform a most curious manoeuvre.

Instead of just opening a flap of his skull as the specialist had intended to do, he had to take the entire top of the man's head off. This was because when he had begun the operation he had seen something that was not on the photograph he had taken. He had seen, inside the man's head, a baby's foot.

He hadn't known what to do, but the foot had started kicking (which was probably the source of the man's headache in the first place, he explained), and the more it kicked, the sicker the man got. They had tried to get the baby out without harming the man further, but his vital signs started failing before this could be done, and so the decision had been taken to remove the top of his head to free the baby.

Imagine his surprise, the specialist told the weeping woman. He had never seen anything like it in his whole career. There was simply no parallel to it. The baby, a girl, was perfectly healthy. Her umbilical cord ran into the man's spinal cord (at this point he realised he was upsetting the woman more than was strictly necessary). He asked if she would like to see the child.

Still weeping the woman was led down stairs and through corridors to the maternity wing of the hospital. There she saw the girl, who was very strong and had a shrill cry, and, in spite of her grief, the woman smiled and held out her arms to the child. It had the man's eyes, she realised, and it had her nose and chin. The girl settled down happily in the woman's arms, and, for the first time since she had heard the terrible news, the woman caught herself wondering what the weather was like in the valley, and whether the swifts had returned to their home.

Nasim Marie Jafry

THE LION POSE

I was waiting for a bus, on my way to my dream therapy class. It was freezing cold, one of those nights when the cold just creeps into your bones no matter how many layers you're wearing. There was an old woman standing in the doorway of the video store next to the bus-stop. She was about seventy, wearing a blue baseball cap, brown fur boots and a see-through plastic raincoat. She wore big white plastic beads *over* the raincoat. She was shouting obscenities at everyone who passed by and sticking her tongue out as far as it would go. She looked like she was doing the lion pose, a yoga position where you stretch out your tongue, eyes wide, fingers splayed. It's good for insanity. When the bus came I got on and looked back at the old woman ranting and retching in the lion pose.

I was still thinking about her when I got to my dream class. The class was taken by a Californian woman called Shandra who had piercing blue eyes and copper bangles. I had nick-named her Chardonnay. There were six of us in the group, five women and one man, all divorced except me. I was recently dumped, but I hadn't been married. We would share our dreams, and Chardonnay would help us channel our dream energies to make healthy changes in our sad lives. Ray went first. Ray's wife had left him when he was in hospital having a haemorrhoids operation. He had a recurring dream that he was spooning ice-cream into his arse. Ray didn't say arse, he said anus. Chardonnay thought Ray was blocked. My dream was dull by comparison. I was at my ex-lover's wedding and I spat on his bride. Chardonnay thought I was having trouble letting go. Sometimes, Ray and I would go for a drink after the class, but I didn't feel like it tonight. I knew he fancied me, and it made me a bit uncomfortable.

I waited for my bus home. There were two other people of mixed race waiting. I notice these things. A wee black boy with his white mother, and a dark-skinned baby strapped onto her white mother's back. The lack of ethnic diversity in this city scares me. People say it's cosmopolitan here, but it's only cosmopolitan because of the tourists. Take away the castle and the festival, and this city would lose its colour.

I have a Scottish mother and a Pakistani father. My

Lanarkshire genes and accent did not protect me from being called a black bastard when I was at school. I would answer in my shaky wee eleven year old voice, I'm not black, I'm light brown. There was a Chinese boy in third year. He was also a black bastard. English boys were poofs, English girls were snobs. The day my wee brother, Joe, started secondary school some boys tried to flush his head down the toilet. The janitor with the ginger hair broke up the scuffle.

We'll get you at four, you Paki bastard.

The threat of being battered after the bell became a routine. They never actually did anything, but it got so bad that Joe was too scared to go to school. In the mornings he would sit in the front garden with his uniform on and refuse to budge. My mother went up to the school and the head-master spoke to her in hushed tones. The modern studies teacher kept me behind after class once and told me if I ever got any hassle to tell him, and he'd sort it out. I was too scared to tell him about the time a boy called me a nigger for the whole bus journey home. My friends sat beside me, enduring the nigger litany, but they were too scared to say anything either.

When Joe was in second year a miracle occurred. The toughest boy in the school, Ian Mackenzie, a punk who wore a studded collar and had been in a borstal for attempted murder, so the story went, took Joe under his wing. No-one ever bullied him again. Ian Mackenzie gave Joe back his confidence and introduced him to the Sex Pistols.

I smiled at the wee boy at the bus-stop and wondered what kind of shit he got in the play-ground.

I look Asian, although some people think I'm Italian. When I lived in San Francisco, Americans were fascinated by my accent and appearance.

Wow, that's such a cool accent, where are you from?

I'm from Scotland. I'm half Pakistani.

Wow, do you speak *Scottish* and *Pakistani*? (We're talking Stanford graduate here.)

No, I just speak English.

Wow, your accent is so cool!

Thank-you.

You get to feel so fucking special living in the States. I'm sure I could have been excused from being mugged and shot if I had said, well actually I'm half Scottish and half Pakistani.

The worst thing my Scottish mother ever did was give me her frizzy hair. The worst thing my Pakistani father ever did was kill himself when I was eight. I was at a Halloween party at the Brownies, ducking for apples. When I got home my alcoholic daddy was dead. I had been dressed up as a doctor and was wearing his old stethoscope round my neck.

I find it hard to let go of relationships, I need to say goodbye a lot. They tell me I'm beautiful, they tell me they love me, I tell them I love you, then they leave me. Nine months ago my lover, an Irish artist in San Francisco, told me that he didn't love me enough to stay in the relationship. We were in the kitchen at the time.

I wanted to be dead. I bought razor blades just to get me over the impulse. A wee nick in the leg was just *enough* violence against myself to get me away from the idea. I dabbed the scarlet droplets which oozed from my leg with white toilet paper. I liked the red stain on the white tissue. I performed this ritual several times over the next few weeks.

Instead of killing myself I moved to Edinburgh. My artist took me to the airport. It was sadder than the final scene in Dr Zhivago. We clung to each other and wept. On the flight back to Heathrow I kept going into the toilet so that I could cry. When we landed ten hours later, I was still greeting.

I was in touch with him a lot.

Letters,

postcards (so's he'd *have* to read them),

answering machine messages,

e.mail,

faxes.

He wrote back to me once, saying that he too had lost a lot, and that he cried when he looked at photos of me. He had only started seeing someone so soon after our break-up because he couldn't stand being alone, and no, he never wanted to get back together. He hoped that we had both learned and grown from our four years together.

I found a stash of porn magazines in the garage a month before we broke up. Why couldn't you wank over Vogue or Cosmopolitan or photos of me? I screamed. I'm really sorry, it's just something men do, he said. I imagined him standing in a queue to pay for his copy of Playboy, and I wanted to throw up.

When I lived in San Francisco I worked at a day centre for adults with neurological problems. I became close to Nora, a young Mexican woman badly affected by MS and delusions. People said we looked like sisters. Nora's explanation for her paralysis was that she was an angel whose wings had been clipped by falling through a hole in the ozone layer. Her favourite colour was sky-blue. I called her the blue angel lady. When I told her that my Irish artist had broken up with me, she said tearfully, But have you told him you love him, has he seen your tears? She was passionately in love with her male nurse and had the wedding planned. Nora and I shared some delusions.

I was back in San Francisco recently, visiting my friend, Amelia. Amelia is in love with a perfectly sculpted Norwegian systems analyst. Amelia is one of those people that you feel happy just being around. She's always smiling. Amelia doesn't look back. Her last boyfriend asked her to marry him and then moved out. She never saw him again. I would have been camping on his doorstep, prostrate with grief. Amelia was policing my movements, so I called the artist when she was at work. I told him that it was important to me to say goodbye again. He said that he had removed me from his life nine months ago, had no desire to see me, and furthermore it would upset his new lover if he saw me. I begged him to see me, and he hung up.

A high point of my visit was seeing Nora. I dropped into the centre during an art therapy class. We made a Halloween mask, an owl's face. Nora could not move her hands, so she would tell me what to do. She insisted that the owl have a beauty spot on its right cheek (do owls have cheeks? I asked her, neither of us knew) to match her own. I sifted through hundreds of sequins to find a sky-blue one, and we used that for the owl's mole. I cried when I said goodbye to her.

The weekend before I came back to Edinburgh I went over to the artist's flat, the flat that we had chosen together. I called first just to be polite. He said he had company and hung up.

He saw me coming along the street and shut the blinds. I rang the bell a couple of times, calmly, like the post-man. He did not answer. I knew she was in there. This would have been a good time for the lion pose. I sat on the doorstep in fight-or-flight mode, not sure which one to choose. I was deciding how best to use this surge of adrenaline when Tim arrived, jogging.

Tim was my old neighbour. Hi, Tim, I said. Tim did not seem surprised to find me there, ashen-faced on the doorstep, after nine months absence. Can I come in for a glass of water, I'm feeling a bit upset? I went upstairs and was greeted by Tim's gay flatmates and their boyfriends, all going about their Saturday morning business. I explained that my once lover was barricading himself in the apartment, afraid to open the door to me. It happens, honey, they said. They gave me blueberry pancakes and coffee, and I felt better.

When I left Tim's flat the artist's car was still there, so I tried the doorbell again. He did not answer. I peered into his car to see if there were any traces of a female passenger. There was a hair-brush with blonde hair on the seat. Bastard, I shouted up to the living room window and walked bravely down the hill. I turned back once, half-expecting to see him silhouetted in the window like Norman Bates, but there was no-one there.

The fax-machine was blinking furiously when I got home from work today. Amelia's big, bold, happy writing leapt out from the flimsy tongue of paper. I ripped the fax from the machine.

> Lizzie, I wanted to let you know before anyone else did. I ran into James and his woman at an opening last night. Jesus Christ, they're getting married. He's such an asshole. Forget him. She just doesn't sparkle like you. She's short and blonde with no dress sense. I love you, I miss you. Call me.

I wailed, crumpling the fax into a ball, and threw it across the kitchen. My stomach twisted, and I ran to the bathroom. Nothing came up. The smell of the toilet water made me feel even more sick. I retched and sobbed into the porcelain until it was dark.

I got up still snivelling and switched on the light. I squinted at my groggy reflection in the cabinet mirror. I stuck out my tongue and splayed my fingers. Again and again and again.

I am a lion. I am posing. Ha ha ha.

The immense pain was still there. It would take something bigger than a lion to shift it. I slid back the cabinet door and reached in, weary.

A.B. Jackson

THE CHRISTMAS PET

A blood-sport refugee
Kicking its heels in sanctuary.
It was an impulse buy,

Spurred on by the children
And the straw season.
Care required, minimum:

Recommended food, anything,
Make the den inviting,
Give the gold nose-ring

A good polish.
It did not flourish;
I offered barley and mash

Without success. It grew
Lean and repetitive, slow,
Lean and repetitive. Now,

Having churned up the lawn,
It patrols
The small circle of indoors

Scoring things with precise horns.

VALENTINE

Let's just say it crawled across the snow.
On York Road, Dublin 6, moonlight flashed
Upon the slate roof-tiles as I passed,
Neck and neck with light, heading home;
Found Robert Furey at the cash machine,
Beer-happy, vague, my phone number inked
On his fist, Louise woozy, arms linked,
Her Valentine's Day trousers blue and cream;
Myself showered and shaved, in my pocket
A new bar of Kinder Bueno chocolate,
My fingers ochre from tobacco,
I left them with a dance, a half-arsed fling.
Let's just say it crawled across the snow,
Shaved with light, intent. A telephone rings.

IN MEMORY OF R.D. LAING
(d. Aug. 1989)

Painted meate no hunger feedes,
Dying life each death exceeds.
Robert Southwell

You didn't leave us with much. A sour taste,
An honest child's vision of a naked king,
Two-bit dramas in ruined amphitheatres.
A sense of loss provoked by life this time.

You, at least, saved your death for the end,
Reduced it to the bare bones of matter
While redefining ours: compatible
With breathing, making love or tea or money.

Not to be undone, we, in a stagnant
Paradise of todays, whitewash our recent
Pasts with our recent wallpaper, reduce
To Fashionable or Unfashionable. Escape

Your passion with some cushioning cliches:
'The insane are sane and vice versa?
Obvious trash.' This was not your message.
You saw a man whose muscles turned to bone.

And this was Man, dear god, just petrified
Mass from which the eyes stared out. Our insides
Foreign, denying themselves in us, we rest
Expelled among our bought things and our screens.

So who or what to blame? Genealogist
Of pain, you hauled the Family up for trial.
No accident, surely, that this should come
From a Protestant Scot, religion sprung

From Calvin, Luther, constipation's martyrs,
All out-pouring viewed with suspicion.
Of course we weep as European walls
Are broken. How could we dance? There's freedom

And there's freedom. Ours is a well-stocked fridge,
Jacob's ladders rising to the boardroom,
Cheap air miles. Locked in level pressure,
One by one we have hijacked ourselves.

Demands? Just this: that the long not feeling
At home should end. Distance. Unbalance. No
Wonder. We've placed so much faith in the air
And the air is so silent now we're so well

And truly in it, taking brief snapshots
Of Earth from orbit. Earth so far from touch,
A world below that grows to nought, as systems
Fail their checks, and links are lost, and we find Space.

Goodbye body. The mind's out on a limb.
What else could we do but close ranks among
Mutual conspiracies of the heart,
We, the half-baked, eternal unmarried,

Salvation or nemesis lying wholly
With dear ones loved to death? Create, you said.
And here was room for praise: Art's descent,
Unearthing the heart's apocryphal text

In Christ's long shadow, growing darker still
Against our legislation of the light.
We cast our own divisions in the sun,
Before, behind, within, each way we turn.

Your arrival, timed to imperfection,
Was rude but not uncalled for, offering us
This: the unconditional chance to be
And be misunderstood beyond all guilt.

Hopefully we can return the favour,
Forgive you for finding a refuge in booze
Being lost in the soul's church torn by factions,
Angry with God for so hiding His face.

Yes you wanted Him, more than most; argued
For angels in Glasgow, London, Iona.
The truth is you ran with us all, but looked back.
And we froze

David Kinloch

BRAVEHEART

O Mel! Mel of the hair extenders! Braveheart!
O Mad Mac Mel! It is I,
Walt, Walt Whitman, who salutes you.
When I heard at the close of the day
That your heroic film of the Wallace
Would premiere in Stirling, I floated

From Mount Florida, high above Glasgow, floated
From the residence of my comrade Kinloch, a brave heart
Like you, I crossed the hummock-land of Shotts as Wallace
Did on leaving Elderslie, I
Sped through the dun-coloured upland (beside the great M8)
                                                    that day
To celebrate your epic but most of all to be with you

O Mel! But also to petition you,
Dark singer of Democracy, you who floated
Like a Moses through Scottish bogs, waiting for the day
To release your noble, simple people, their brave brave heart
Clasped in an English vice. O Mel, I
Confuse you, mix you in my mind with Wallace.

And who could blame me? For you and Wallace
Commingle in my scented breast, you
Two and I, comrades all, shooting the film of liberty I
Crave above all else, I crave and lost as my successors floated
Back up stream to a land of villanelles and sonnets. Bravehearts!
Brave Walt! a bearded Ariel imprisoned in a bad sestina who
                                                    would this day

Be free again by your example, free today
To live today, to sing the love of comrades as Wallace
Did. He could not rhyme, his only beat the braveheart
Quad-pumping the eclectic plaid about his knees (What knees!).
                                                    You
Saw him Mel, as clearly as I see you who floated
From Australia via Hollywood to this premiere. I

Name the perfumed guests as they arrive, I
Shake the manly hand of Jodie Foster, day
Dream as Christian Slater – he of the slow doe-eyes – floats
In. We sit transfixed as the credits of your Wallace
Roll but I have eyes alone for you,
Peach of a biceps – your musk white thighs – muncher of
power-breakfasts – Braveheart!

Mel Wallace, Will Gibson, this day
Your barbaric yawp injects its braveheart
Into me. You and I floating and free.

WI HIS DICKY-BOW
fae the French o Josée Lapeyrère

Wi his dicky-bow black as a
keeker the ref jigs
hauns still as deid mackerel
fists scrunched as a stane
aboot the boxers ach! his 'BREAK!'

unties their clinch
– 'YER AS SLAW AS A WEE
LASSIE MAN!' – widny they
jist each o the two o them
jist luv tae banjo
the crap-bag an puntie-up
owre the ither side aw
cockie-like but

its the huggin stoaps em
lumberin the ither's airms
cheek fur chowl their big
rid gloves are Mickey's ears
aw bloody aboot the gills an oan
the sheen o the sassenach's shouder

an the daurk behind the cords
o the ring hotchin wi faces:
'HAW COCKYNUT-HEID
DINNAE JIST STAUN THER
LIKE A FART IN A TRANCE
WEE MASIE SEYS GET TORE

IN MELT THE BUGGER' ah luv
tae see yon douce hardman
yon big stumer o a mainiger
wi his saft jessie hauns
his shuge yeller sponge
his gob in the lug o the
boxer close up close up
a wheesht a caress
'screw the nut oan ye go get steamed right intae him'

Norman Kreitman

FISHING WITH NORMAN MacCAIG

Each time I called for him he was perfectly ready,
equipment checked and in smooth order,
pared to essentials. And I, cluttered with gadgets,
would clatter behind as he led the way downstairs.

In the boat, as befits a sedulous angler,
he was taciturn, though between essential words
he would give that courteous, gentle smile
that was his signature, before his gaze returned

to the contemplation of water. And when
in his own good time he hooked a trout
he'd eye it dispassionately, as one whose life was spent
retrieving silver from all the elements of Scotland.

BIRDS OF SOUTHERN AFRICA

... and coming out of the night sky
in which all of us are pinholes
I touch down with the names

> *golden oriole, blacksmith plover, helmet shrike*
> *the lilac-breasted roller*

which fix a man's experience for an hour,
which direct his eye

> *goliath heron, sociable weaver and red-billed teal,*
> *the pearly-spotted owl*

where excited whispers point, binoculars lift
to a magic circle

> *sacred ibis, common swift, Cape batis*
> *the fork-tailed dorongo*

and the awe-struck visitor gazes at the resident
or a transient more exotic than himself

> *tawny eagle, red-eyed dove, trumpeter hornbill,*
> *flycatcher of paradise*

until it flashes away on the wind,
colours chiming like syllables
at the intersection of a living day
and the view from nowhere ...

Gerry Loose

THE LONG LUNCH
for Caroline O'Toole (& Frank O'Hara)

after lunch at the Tron
I smoked a cigarette

we moved table for that
& your lips moved just so

when my friends arrived
we moved table but the baby

Caitlin was not let in the bar
we moved table

& your smile moved just so
my friend's baby moved us

as you   that time   listened
then your friend and her

daughter Caitlin showed   by chance
and we moved chairs

I moved table
& smoked a cigarette

the while watching
friends   you

it may be that coincidence
is the trust we put in each other

from coincidence we
make what we will

what we will is a trust
a lunch where all tables

are vacant reserved   strange
friendships Frank   when you (dead)

talk to me   & Caroline
you hear   & now   I

speak to you both directly
what is taking place here

FOR KATE ON HER BIRTHDAY

I wake one morning
to the sound of traffic and the cackling of gulls
I have mislaid my seventeenth wedding anniversary
this scene is acted out in three thousand bedrooms this morning

we are happened upon
yet small things still retain the power to please
the purchase of a packet of envelopes
the memory of another bedroom window elsewhere

nothing can ever be subtracted
what is not clear is how
with the clouds flying overhead
we avoid the shadows

Roddy Lumsden

AFTER ENTOMOLOGY

This getting to know you isn't easy,
Like fathoming again the difference
Between those insects which come in
At the roadside front of the house,
Those which appear from a clear
And verdant stasis round the back,

Then those which are, at times, found
Struggling against the surface tension
In the toilet bowl at the house's centre:
Which are entered as Unclassifiable
In my daybook. After entomology,
My two-leggedness, my lax vanity,

My burdened notion of an inbetween:
The black week when the theatre lies
Unvisited or those amassed seconds
Of radio dead-time, the notes which
Skirl ahead while the piper breathes
Or treading water, knowing you'll be saved.

HOBBLEDEHOY

Horses passing the window there, one night,
Were tricks of stereo – a recent invention.
I had my mono to fall back on – a song
For the great aunts, and a mitt with which
To circle for the fee.
                                    The market garden
Spread east towards The Honky Tonk estate.
The catty miasma of flowering currant,
Hothouses rowed with red-hot pokers
And crimson ballerinas, potting sheds where
Bulbs lay centred in loam: these things rally.
A mildew foust which hangs calm in the gents
At St James, as I fasten up my spare,
Has triggered this; Balmullo.
                                        All's well until
That single flashback I cannot account for:
The awkward girl coming up the length
Of pleached hedge as I turn from the window
To grasp the tablecloth's end and pull,
Aware that I've not yet mastered the trick.

Brian McCabe

RAT

My hand discovers you – a scrap
of doormat with claws, scrubbingbrush
with teeth, among leaves, old sacks
in the world's most unlit outhouse.
I am a bellows that sucks the air,
as the breath rushes into me
like a hunting thing, scared
of you, and of what you are not.
Hardened to the brittle, the literal
emblem of yourself. That pebble
embedded in your side is more
alive in its cool, smooth silence.
With a stick, I pick you up
by a tail as still as a coathook.
Did death catch you on the hop
old enemy – as it catches those
who make a habit of survival?
I won't pick up that, I think.
Then your eyeless eye's fullstop
stops me – mid-life, mid-thought –
with the riddle of your dry reminder.
I shut my eyes as I throw you
as far as I can throw your image
out of my mind's out-of-sight.
One morning, I'll find you there
grinning at me, like to like,
from your delicate skeleton.

JAR

You have served to carry our milk
Our provisions our necessary items.
Ashes of our dead, for example:
Broken necklaces; rainwater; barley.

You were good enough to hold
The flowers for the still life.
Even when they wilted to their image
You refrained from comment.

When you glimpsed your immortality
(Before it was turned to the wall)
Your lip did not tremble –
You waited to be emptied, to be filled.

Forgive us urn we were blind
To your virtues: solidity; emptiness.
Perhaps it was in your best interests
That we saw only your purpose.

From the childhood of artefacts
You come to me, intact
With your chipped rim your mended crack,
Open-mouthed in a mute plea.

Let me place my hand
On your rounded shoulder.
Set my ear to your chasm to hear
The long, boring story of the abyss.

Let me fill you
With more than my voice:
Dumb clay drum, dumb clay drum,
I utter your worth.

And when the inevitable happens and
A rebellious elbow, a gesturing wrist,
Coups you from your ledge of being,
Somersaulting you into becoming –

Rest assured jar, I will enact
Those animated antics of distress,
Trying to catch you
Before you smash.

MOTH

Landing on the television screen
she proceeds to explore
the chinless chin
of the Secretary of State for Scotland –
just as he is arguing for
the tradition of the union.

The moth settles down between
his nose and his upper lip
and spreads her wings –
giving him a black,
diligently trimmed
and very famous moustache.

J. Derrick McClure

A LASSIE'S NA-SAY

Frae Mireille o *Frédéric Mistral, Cant Quatren, stanzas 65-71.*
Owerset frae the Provençal by J. Derrick McClure.

The bonnie quine, yon simmer morn,
Wes sat her leen aside the burn,
Her sleeves rowed up, her skirt abeen the knee.
Giein the caps a reenge an syne
Wi taits o girse tae gar them shine –
The stripe rowed ower her feeties fine –
Fegs, wes she nae a loesome sicht tae see!

Said Elshie, 'Fair gweed day, my dou!
Synin your cappies, are ye nou?
In this skyre burnie's watter, dae ye think
My braa fite bull cud slock his drouth?'
Said Mirren, 'Weel, I'm seer there fouth
O watter here! In aa this routh
Jist gie your baestie aa it likes tae drink.'

'My dou,' the wilsome birkie cried,
'Gin ye sud traik, or come as bride,
Tae Cullentrye, far souns the fite swaws' sang,
My dou, sic dargs ye ne'er wad dree!
For yon's far kye o keir-blaik blee
Sae baal an crouse, gaes vaigin free:
They need nae tent, an lassies thinks na lang!'

'My lad, amo your kye, I dreid,
A quine wad weary maist tae deid!'
'My dou, fowk dinna weary fan there twa!'
'My lad, for fowk that's faur frae hame
Sharra's the watter tae their wame,
Harsk tae their lyre the het sin's glame!'
'My dou, the fir-trees' scug is cweel an braa.'

'My lad, your fir-trees' bous alang,
Crowls nedders green wi pousion't stang!'
'My dou, there faaps an herons sweelin roun;
Ye'll see their lyart manties trail:
Alang the Don the snakes they skail –'
'My lad, I'm wae tae brak your tale:
Ower hyne's your fir-trees frae my hamelt toun.'

'My dou, ye ken the aal word says,
It's ull tae spae far kirkmen gaes,
Or quines, at linth, their daily breid tae pree.'
'My lad, I'd gang, an wadna rue,
Tae pree it wi the lad I loe:
For yon, the nest I daur forhou.'
'Gie your luve than, my bonnie lass, tae me!'

Said Mirren, 'Aye, my lad, ye'll hae't –
Fan yon burr-thrissles by the gait
Growes purpie grapes in tossels hingin doun;
Fan roses frae your gadwann blaa;
Fan muntains mouts lik springtime snaa;
Fan fite-sailed galleys snuves awa
Frae Aaford ower the sea tae Huntly toun!'

Carl MacDougall

ANGELS

She told her Granny she'd seen the angels.

Where were they?

Over by the wash-hoose at the back of the midden.

And how many were there?

Just the four.

And what were they doing?

They were flying about, dead fast, then stopping still, doing nothing; just flying and stopping and hovering in mid-air the way angels always do.

And did anyone else see them?

Ann McAllister said she saw them, but she never saw them at all. She said one of them had a halo and none of them had haloes nor nothing like it. They werenae they kind of angels. They were just ordinary angels.

You get yourself washed and ready for school.

She saw them when her Mammy died.

She'd never had a Daddy so she went to stay with her Granny, who told her stories about bringing home the cows and guddling fish with her brother who died in a prisoner of war camp.

I don't know, her Granny said when she asked why her Mammy died. Maybe you could ask a priest.

God wanted her for Himself, said Father Byrne; but she thought that was rotten, for it meant God liked her Mammy but didn't like her. The priest said God loved everybody.

But he must have his favourites, she said, thinking of school.

Father Byrne suggested she should pray to St Jude, the patron saint of hopeless cases, to see if she could get a faith because it was terrible for one so young to lose her faith.

Don't tell him about the angels, her Granny said.

Her Mammy died in a maternity hospital. She knew that because she read the sign and when she asked her Granny she was told to be quiet because the soup was nearly ready.

She asked the nurse. Women come in here to have their babies, she said.

Have their babies what?

To give birth. To have their babies born.
She couldn't understand why her mum went in there.

Sometimes she thought they were lights, as if somebody with a
strong torch was swirling the light around in a dissolving pattern. Or they were like fireworks, a whoosh and a trail of
coloured lights and sparks, except there wasn't any sound.

Mostly they were like themselves. Small and compact,
silent and very fast.

They had lovely little faces, she imagined they might have
been drawn by a cartoonist, and tight little wings. Not that you
could see them. They were in a blur, but you could tell the
wings were there because of the haze they created, especially in
front of a light. They altered the atmosphere, like heat rising.

They were neither coloured nor dressed, nor did they
speak. The angels simply came and disappeared. And no one
told her; she knew they were angels.

When she saw them on the stairs her Granny said they
were getting nearer.

Granny, are you going to die?
Certainly not.
How do you know?
Cause I don't smoke and I only have a wee toddy at night
afore I go to my bed and I look after you and eat soup that
sticks tae my ribs.
I thought they angels were coming for you.
Angels have got better things to do with their time than
come running after the likes of me. And even if they were for
me, I'd keep them waiting.
Why are they here but?
If you ask me, I think your Mammy sent them.
Have you seen angels, Granny?
During the war there were angels here aa the time.
Did the Americans bring them?
Not at all.
Do rich folk see angels?
I don't know anything about rich folk.

Then one night when they danced around her room and she
could hear her Granny sleeping in the bed by the door, she
thought she knew why the angels were there.

They whizzed and tumbled, capered round the bare light bulb, hovered, smiled and moved through the glass as if it was space itself, as though the moon, the night and the stars in the sky were fixed and painted behind the glass She knew the room was cold, but the angels made her warm, made her want to sing with excitement.

She tried to stifle a little cry. When it escaped she hoped the angels wouldn't hear, hoped they would not be frightened.

Then it happened.

She closed her eyes and felt herself rise, felt her body lift from the bed and the covers slip away as she tumbled with the angels. All around was light and warmth, as if a star had shattered, as if she was being carried gently forward, moved from one peace to another. She rocked and floated, afraid to open her eyes in case the spell would be broken, afraid even to breathe.

They were beneath and around her. She felt them bear her body upwards and away, felt their support. She was one of them; the way her Granny said she felt when she ran through the briars to catch the hens, or watched the cows move up the road by themselves in the evening.

In the morning she was back in bed and could not remember going to sleep. Something had changed. She knew it, but could not tell her Gran because she didn't know what was there before.

She drank her tea and watched her Gran make scrambled eggs, watched the way the bits of the egg joined to become pale yellow, and how everything changed when it was cooked.

You make the toast.

That was another change, she thought, from cold to hot, grey to brown, soft to hard. And the margarine changed things even more, altering itself, from solid to liquid in the process.

She told her Granny, who sighed. It's the angels, she said, the same as the angels. Will they be there forever?

They'll go away and leave and no come back if you don't eat your scrambled eggs, said Granny.

Kevin McFadden

AGAMEMNON TOWELS OFF

Triumph's first indulgence is a bath.
Soldiers home with laurels mount their spears
above the hearth, draw water. Victories
go horizontal. Someone leaves the linen
stacked as innocent as soaps
or oily fragrances or treatments
unsuspicious placed in flaccid reach
of dripping limbs.

I might have had a fighting chance if only
I had taken showers. No regrets.
The underworld is overflown with famous
underestimates. Submerged here,
once successful men still sponge
the sundry wounds, compare their
gaping, daggered backs:
a husband wet, a general slain
who came, who saw, who conquered, who
relaxed.

Donal McLaughlin

A CHANGE OF SCENERY

He closed the door behind them and leaned against it. Connor
O'Doherty was now alone in his son's flat. It had taken a
whole song and dance first but, right enough. After him getting
up out of his bed and driving the rest of them over for just after
lunchtime as well!

You got no bloody gratitude. None whatsoever.

If he was being honest, young Brendan had made it pretty
obvious he didn't want him there, couldn't handle the thought
of him being there alone.

That was the thanks you got for rearing them.

He'd only actually gone when his mother nudged him out,
probably saying something like 'Offer it up!' or 'Do it for me.'

Typical.

Tough.

On his way back into the livingroom a draught hit him. It was
blowing a gale through the flat. He went round closing the
windows, stopping only to look at the bedroom again. There
was definitely something about them bedclothes.

When he got back to the livingroom, he didn't park his
bum where his son had made him sit. Not on your nelly, he
was going to make himself comfortable in that one there, in
front of the TV, instead. The radio was still on in the kitchen.
He'd asked for it as soon as he'd come in and caught some of
the comments and analysis before the matches started. If he
was lucky, he might get a good race now on TV, the English
results would come up at the bottom of the screen, and if there
was any goals in the Scottish games, he was sure to pick up on
it from the kitchen. He managed to get a picture up with the
remote control. Good on ye, boyo! Aye, he could take to this.
He was beginning to like the flat better, now there was a bit of
life about it.

He got another fag going. There wasn't an ashtray so he
took a dish from beneath a plant. God knows what the young
fella saw in plants anyway. It was like a bloody jungle in here,
and it wasn't as if he'd a woman to look after them. That one
there's a weeping willow, no – I tell a lie – a weeping fig, that's
what it is. Aye, the old boy still knew these things. They

needn't go thinking he didn't. They'd another thing coming to them if they did.

'And it's over to Parkhead where I think we have a sensational equaliser for Forfar Athletic against Celtic –'

'Yes, Tom, it's Celtic 1 Forfar 1 and' *Shite*. Connor raced round the door and turned the bloody thing off. It was the friggin board's fault. When he thought back to the Celtic team when he'd first moved over. All them years in a row. Different story these days. Buckin bucket team, getting stuffed week in week out.

He decided to make himself a cup of tea while he was there. Jaysus Christ Almighty, has he no friggin Tetleys like the rest of humanity? He found them. Bugger's got no milk but. You can forget the biscuits, too, by the look of things. It's an English cup of tea you'll be having.

He sat down at the window to drink it, sat blowing over it first. Nice view out there, right enough. He could've sat all day, just watching what was going on in them other flats. He wished he knew how the young'uns managed it: how they put the money together for places like this. Changed days, so it was.

There was no sign of Brendan getting married either. As bad as his brothers getting. And he'd told his Granny, God have mercy on her, a lie. He always told her he'd be married when he was 23. The same one had known some lovely wee girls, too. Bernie had met them or spoken to them on the phone. Connor had told him, whether he liked it or not: *it wasn't right*. Sure when he was his age, he was the father of six – and Brendan was one of them.

Connor didn't agree with this own-flat business either. In his day, you stayed wi' your mother and father until you got married, full stop. He'd told his wee girls what would happen to them if they got pregnant. Or rather: what he'd do to the young fella, more like. It was different with the boys. Still against their religion but.

Ye wouldn't think this was him in Edinburgh! He would rather be back in the house, to be quite honest.

Now he thought about it, he'd never been one for travelling. Sure he'd never set foot out of Ireland before they emigrated. And all the years he was in Scotland, he'd never went anywhere, never saw anything. Well maybe the Supporters' Bus to away games but you don't see much that way. The inside of the Hibs before you left and that was about it.

This country couldn't begin to compare wi' Ireland anyway.

Then, right enough, a couple of years ago, he'd gone through a travelling phase. Suddenly, he was up and out and around the country, visiting his daughters and sons-in-law. The wedding would hardly be over and he'd be away off to visit them. His daughters were chuffed, and it made him feel good. He took Bernie with him, of course, drove her everywhere. Folk thought it was lovely. That it did him good to get out of the house. That maybe he could handle it after all, if he got his voluntary redundancy.

The only thing about trips like that but was: you were always in somebody else's house. He wasn't comfortable with it being John's house, like. Or Brian's. You had to hand it to him but: one thing he always did was christen the bed in the spare room for them. The first night in whichever of the houses it was, and he would make sure him and Bernie did it. Bernie was always against it, but she'd give in before she'd let say Bernadette and John think they could hear them arguing.

Bernie was needlessly ashamed about it. Them was the very words he'd said to her: *needlessly ashamed*. 'Sure they know about these things now. They're adults – married!' he'd told her. Bernie's face had relaxed a bit when she heard that. 'And anyway, they're probably doing it as well!' he added. The poor woman had gone beetroot.

He himself had only laughed.

The horses. He should get back to the 3.45 from Newmarket, see if Limavady Laddie made it. 3-1, the boy was. Pity he'd not got to the bookies.

On his way through the hall, he noticed there was no Holy Water font. It was the same in the boy's old flat in Airdrie. He'd gone to bliss himself on the way out and there was no Holy Water font. This flat was the same. Not a single Holy Picture to be seen anywhere. It wasn't right. He didn't want the boy losing his religion, people saying he hadn't brought him up properly. Not a single Holy Picture, by Christ. He would never've got away wi' it over home.

Sometimes Connor wondered whether he'd done the right thing in taking the family away from Ireland. Troubles or no

Troubles. Sometimes, listening to them, ye would never know his lot were Irish.

He sighed as he sat down. Still just the adverts.

He trusted his wee girls to go to Mass all right. He was sure they did, even if two of them had gone'n'married Protestants, Scotch boys, after him always saying and all about Irish boys being far nicer, and them always agreeing. As for Brendan but, he probably couldn't tell ye the name of his parish priest, never mind what the gospel was about on Sunday. *I noticed he never went to Communion on Christmas Day.* His mother did too, she just wouldn't admit it. The bugger hadn't taken him on at the dinner table but, when he'd said about hoping they were still all going to confession every fortnight, or had at least been in preparation for the celebration of the birth of Our Lord.

There's the boy who rides Niamh's Song now.

Some wee dander that is. They still weren't back. Must bloody well be climbing Arthur while they're at it.

It occurred to him that maybe he should go round opening the windows again before they got back. Brendan could be funny about things like that. Them looks of his were lethal. Obviously didn't slap him hard enough when he was younger. That's what the mistake I made was, where I must've went wrong.

He started with the bedroom first. The boy slept at the back, it would be quieter than onto the street at the front. Connor opened the door. Them bedclothes again. There was something about them. The colours. The pattern. Like he was advertising something. The fact it was a double bed and all. It was against his religion, would lead him into temptation. Visitors, he'd answered, cool as you like, when Connor asked him what he needed a double bed for. Then: Some of my best friends are couples. Cheeky pup. That was the thing about him. He was that secretive, worse than his older brothers getting, and yet at the same time he tries to tant ye, to tease you.

It was a nice Holy Picture he needed up there, above the bed, married or no married. A Padre Pio at least. Connor had been going to buy him a lovely crucifix thon time at Carfin, his mother wouldn't let me but. The arguments Bernie had given him, into the bargain! He was so a Catholic, he just didn't want stuff like that up in his house, she'd said. He didn't want to be shoving it down the throats of anybody coming into the house. I don't know, the way that young fella thinks at times.

He wouldn't even let you give him the Praying Hands. Bernie had spotted these lovely Praying Hands for him when she was over in Knock herself wi' Dawn and she was going to take them for him. And she was right, sure they could be Protestant Praying Hands as well, so they wouldn't offend no-one, but no: according to Dawn, Brendan had said he wasn't having the Hands or even *Footprints* on his walls. Have you ever heard the like?

Jaysus, this window was a bugger. He didn't know how the boy got it open first thing in the morning.
                          HOLY GOD!
he knew sometimes he thought he was seeing things but thon was a bare arse, if ever he saw one, in thon there window over there!
          JAYSUS, MARY, AND SAINT JOSEPH!
Connor retreated and sat down on the side of the bed furthest from the window. He tried to light another fag but his fingers were all over the place. It was so, it was a young fella taking a shower and he had the window up as far as it would go. God forgive him and pardon him. Had he no shame, the bugger? It wasn't just his backside he was showing either. Connor's eyesight wasn't good enough to make his mickey out, but when he turned to the side or even right round, the dark hair was unmistakable.
    UN-mistakable.
Why didn't the young fella have a shower-curtain like everyone else if he wanted the window open cos of condensation or whatever? Connor could've understood that, now.

Right, he was going to sit here and watch and see what else he got up to.
Connor couldn't credit it: your man was just standing there, turning this way, then that. After a while, a blue bath-towel flashed around in the gap. Next thing, the young fella started to shave or something, to inspect his neck anyway, at what was probably a wash-hand basin on the wall at the window. Then he disappeared altogether. He turned up almost immediately in the room next door but. When he did, it was obvious the towel was round his shoulders and down his back, but even though the bedroom window was up as high as the other one, he came right over to it and Connor caught an eye-

ful. He turned away, quick, and pretended to be looking for Radio Eireann on his son's ghettoblaster.

Connor could now see him in Brendan's mirror, on the chest of drawers. He was sitting down with his bare back to the window, but Connor could tell from the movements that he was putting clean underclothing on. He stood up as he pulled on one of them long baggy T-shirts, young Brendan wore them too, but just as it was falling down over him, a wee girl came into the room, came over towards him, pointing at him, and must have caught him on the chest cos he came falling backwards onto the bed at the window, and the next thing, Holy Jesus, she was on top of him. Holy God. Connor fiddled like mad for Radio Eireann. That was one good thing about Paisley: at least you got good reception for Radio Eireann.

He gave up. He would just have to settle for Radio Scotland. They were in the middle of the classified football results. When he dared to look in the mirror again, the wee girl was still on top of him. She was wearing a pink T-shirt and had plenty to fill it wi'. Both her arms went straight down at an angle. Connor could imagine her pinning him down on the bed.

The T-shirt came off – the young fella's, that is. Connor watched her pull it up over his back and then push him down again. Her head went down, maybe to kiss him. Then up again. And down again. He saw quick flashes of them as they rolled along the bed one way, then the other. She made sure she stayed on top, then disappeared.

Reports were coming in from around the country but Connor was hardly listening. His foot was itching. He removed his shoe and sock and rubbed between his wee toe and the one next to it. The sensation went through him. He was keeping an eye on the mirror. There was nothing to see at the moment. He knew they were still there, but. He'd've seen them going away if they had've.

It was a good while before your woman sat up again. She was still wearing the T-shirt. Holy God, plenty happening, and she still hadn't taken it off for the young fella. Someone turned up at the toilet next door and stood at it, even though it seemed to be another wee girl.

Connor was rubbing away at his foot. He'd be drawing blood if he didn't watch. Just as the phone-in started your woman began to bob up and down. She took her top off, showing herself off to the street like that. Connor watched. This was what happened when they didn't have one ounce of religion in them. Her breasts dropped as she struggled to get the top over her head, then she leant down and fell away. Your man half-stood up and you saw the boxers coming down, then he turned and dropped onto her. You saw maybe her knees, but definitely the cheeks of his backside popping up and down above the white of the window ledge. Without stopping, the boy tried to drag the curtain shut, a blue triangle swept across to sort-of half-fill the window, another hand but from down below was just as quick and whipped it straight back again. They were rolling and tumbling, rolling and tumbling, in the sunlight, the breeze. The answers to questions about the Celtic board, meanwhile, were getting nowhere, slowly.

It was the young fella who was now in control. His head shot up and there was a knock at the door. Shit in hell. Connor had expected them to buzz him up through the entry system. The sharp knock was repeated. Flip bloody sake. 'Coming!' he shouted. 'It's okay, I'm coming!' He flicked the switch on the radio off and attempted to get back into his shoe and sock but it wasn't succeeding. He smoothed the duvet, closed the door behind him, and got his backside to the flat door quick.

The telly was still on in the livingroom. He would pretend he'd dozed off.

It wasn't them. It was a woman – good-looking, too! 'Oh – you must be Brendan's father!' she said. 'He's your mirror image. Here, the postman left this downstairs with me for him.'

Connor slipped back into the bedroom. When he looked out, across, full frontals were jumping into their clothes again. It looked like they couldn't do it quick enough.

When the others got back, nothing was said. There was no reason for anything *to be said*, Connor kept trying to remind himself. He was glad once they were in the car and on their way home but.

Days later his son phoned the house. When Bernie answered, all he said was 'Hi, is my Da in?' Bernie thought it strange at the time. When Connor went to the phone, 'What? It's me he wants?' Brendan asked him what the hell he'd been doing in his bedroom listening to Radio Scotland? When Connor denied it, 'I swear to God, son, and I wouldn't tell you a lie now,' his son just went like that: 'Who the hell was it then? Mr Nobody? It wasn't me, like,' and hung up.

Olivia McMahon

CUCHULAIN OUT THE BACK

Walking along streets with lines of houses like these –
Flowers in the windows that never wilt
And plants in the gardens
Like place settings round a dinner table,
Not even the twitch of a curtain or a cat –
I suddenly see myself aged eight
Bringing home Ireland's great mythical hero
From the public library, and I think how
You never know, with fronts like these,
Cuchulain might be out the back.

He was once, on his way to King Conor's Court,
He with his javelin and hurling stick
And sandals with thongs criss-crossing to the knee,
Me with my hoop and socks that never stayed up.
He'd throw his javelin and catch it before it fell,
I'd hit my hoop, struggling to keep it straight.
We'd run and run until I was
No longer a girl in a grubby frock but him.

All this before he slew Culan's hound
And fought and killed a hundred daily at the ford
Though a woman like an eel was tangled in his legs.
Later he would take the heads off the three wizards and witches
And defeat Fergus in the battle for the Brown Bull of Cuailgne.
And later still – and I could hardly bear to think of this –
He would meet the woman who was called
The Washer at the Ford
With woe and mourning
Washing and washing
His clothes crimson with blood
On the eve of battle with Maeve's great army.

I never did reach King Conor's court
Though I ran for several afternoons.
My mother always called me for my tea
Tinned spam and peaches – it was Sunday.

A FEMALE HUMPHREY BOGART

The man in the cafe was looking like a space shuttle ready for
                                                          take-off.
It was a no-smoking zone – I should have disapproved
but I was drifting through the smoke
back to a hoarding high above my head on my way to school.
I was seeing a woman in a red costume stepping out
and underneath her in yellow like her hair:
For Your Throat's Sake Smoke Craven A.
My father always smoked *Players, Players Please,*
It's the Tobacco that Counts.
He kept them in a silver case held down by worn elastic bands
the sort that kept my stockings up,
and when I think about it now his love was like the glow of
                                                          cigarettes
all through my life until he died. But now I'm jumping on
to Valentine's Day and my first love and London fog outside
and inside we're lighting up, two heads, one flame
and then the deep inhaling, smoke filtering down,
slight panic at my daring.
My daily intake soared from five to twenty
before one night, nipping out to buy a pack,
I found myself in Paris among the *Gitanes* and the *Gauloises*
and the *High Life*, or *Eege Leef* as I learnt to say.
And was the long black holder, with 'O' in gold on the side,
                                              before or after this?
'Oh' I said, discovering the 'O',
and looked for Balkan Sobranis (black) to put in it –
'cos otherwise cigarettes to look at were as unromantic as
                                                          their names:
Senior Service, Benson, Capstan, Strand.
Woodbines was a pretty name but the reality was thin
Like match-stick legs and poverty.
And then there was *Abdullah – No Smoking Not Even*
                                    Abdullah – but I never saw one
and even now the word evokes
not cigarettes but an ad inside a theatre programme.
But thinking of names I'm suddenly remembering
Sweet Afton, Flow gently Sweet Afton,

and a summer spent wandering along Dublin streets not
                              knowing who I'd meet.
We met again forty years later in a New York restaurant
me in a grey raincoat and my collar turned up
hoping I looked like some female Humphrey Bogart just
                                   passing through –
without the fag. Not a cigarette between us – we'd given up.
We sat facing each other in the clear air
and he told me not a day had gone by he had not thought of
                                                    me
and I wondered then how much the tobacco had counted.

Kevin MacNeil

ABERDEEN

Union St. The Lemon Tree.
Diamond St. How the sun
sparks off this granite city –
dharmadhatu, bright as you,
your smile, the light in your ever
changing, ever warm, ripening
eyes, like wild fruits, like a million
mica stars coming alive; your
near heat and dazzle shows me
I'm closer to Lewis, closer to source,
a zendo of mirrors and torches
flashing directly, limitless and spontaneous.

dharmadhatu	the true nature of the universe as seen when in an enlightened state, sparkling like a spider's web at dawn
zendo	Buddhist meditation hall

Angus MacPhee

TAL

Thàinig mi tarsaing air tàl an-diugh 's
mi a'glanadh a-mach mo sheòmair-obrach.
Bha e 'na laighe air an ùrlar,
teann air a' Bhlack-and-Decker.

Nach b'iongantach a bhi ga'm faicinn còmhla?

Cha robh air fhàgail de'n tàl ach an ceann-iaruinn 's
e dearg le meirg... ach tha cuimhneam air fhaicinn
ann an làmhan mo sheanar 's e a'togail eithir.
B'ann dubh-ghorm an tàl an là ud 's
e cheart cho geur ris an ràsar...
sliosan-fiodha a'falbh dheth
mar bhleideagan-sneachda.

Saoil dè bha'm bodach air a dheànamh leis a' Bhlack-and-Decker?

Chum m'athair an tàl mar chuimhneachan 's
nuair a bhàsaich esan,
chum mise an tàl mar chuimhneachan.

Cò a thuigeas an tàl na mo dhèidh-sa,
nuair a bhios iad air a'Bhlack-and-Decker
a thilgeil dha'n sgudal?

ADZE

I came across an adze today
as I cleared out my work-shop.
It was lying on the floor
near the Black and Decker.

Strange to see them together.

The iron was all that was left of the adze,
red with rust... but I remember it
in my grandfather's hands as he built a boat.
It was blue-black in those days
and as sharp as a razor...
wood-shavings flying from it
like snow-flakes.

What would the old man have made with the Black-and-Decker?

My father kept the adze as a keep sake
and when he died
I kept the adze as a keep sake.

Who will understand the adze when I go,
when they have thrown the Black and Decker
out into the bin?

Claire MacRae

THE GUTTING LESSON

The burn played dark tunes all night.

We'd fed it fish guts. At dusk, the water gurgling.
The catch came stiff and bloody from the bag.

You took the first and weighed it in your hand.
Your fingers showed, behind the dorsal fin
a pinhead hole. You put the knife in,
slicing up the belly to the head.

The fish opened like a wallet. Inside, a nest of ribbons,
slimy white balloons that stretched and popped
balling into the fist. The water swallowed them up.
Then I took the knife and cut.

That night we ate fresh grilled trout with herbs and lemon.
My aunt chatted as the gas burnt low.
You tapped out the rhythms of the radio
a black thread of blood beneath one nail.

Margaret McSeveney

DOAKIES AN BOOLDERS

Allison an May were spelderd oan the grun, their mithers littin them oot o the hoose fur an oor afore it wis time tae mak the tea. May kent her hair still stank o the kippers she'd watched ower fur the tea last nicht. She hudnae hud a bath fur a week an her face hud hud nae mair than a cat's lick oan accoont o there bein nae watter, bar fur cookin an drinkin. She didnae ken a boadie could hae sae minny smells; cheese atween her taes, fish at her fud, sheep in her hair an somethin she hud nae name fur stuimin fae 'ur lugs. She'd been weirin the same claes fur five days an they smelt o beef drippin an new breid.

Aw day it'd been het an dwamy. Nae biurd cheeped nor lilted. The yin soun wis the yammer o a dowie wean in a hoose fornent the neebourin field; no even a bumbee flichtered near them. Fower weeks hud draggled by wi nut a cloud tae spile the blueness o the Juin sky. Bit the day, the furst o July, the sky'd been mair white than blue, an since mid-morn a licht gowden broch penned up the sun. This wid be the last simmer brek fae skuil fur Allison an May; next year they'd baith be fifteen an lukkin fur work.

Allison hud a haud o a bunch o grass an wis nibblin the sweet juicy bits at the end. May rowed ower oantae her back an flung her airm up an acroass her broo tae beild it fae the blinnin white heat. She could smell the mealie foosty smell fae her oxters an somethin lik pickle fae her airm. Last nicht, ahint the bookies hut, Jacky Doyle telt her he thocht she wis that braw he waantit tae eat her. Noo she wunnert if he waantit a kiss or if he wis in sair need o a guid feed tae foo oot his sherp chilpit face.

'Whit did Jacky Doyle waant ye fur?' speirt Allison as if she could see richt intae May's brain.

Ah jaloused it wis fur a kiss, bit he wis too feart tae ask.'

'Huv ye ever lit a laddie... thingmy... ye ken...?'

May poo'd a haunfi o her lang rid hair fae under her heid an stertit tae plait it. 'Hunners,' she said.

'Hunners? An ye've no hud a wean?... Yer leein!'

'Naw... ye dinnae get weans jist wi kissin.'

'It wisnae kissin Ah meant. Ye ken whit Ah mean! Oor Beth telt me aw aboot it... if ye dinnae waant tae fa' wi a wean ye've nivvir tae lit a laddie dae ony mair than kiss ye or pit his airm aroon yer shoothers... cause it's just leadin thum oan.'

'That's a lee fur a stert, then.'

'How is it?' asked Allison, liftin her heid tae leer at May.

'Ah yince lit a laddie pit his haun up ma jumper an anither time Ah lit wan pit his haun up the inside o ma knickers... an a nivvir fell wi a wean... so there.'

Allison didnae ken whaur tae stert efter sitch a show o ignorance.

'Dae ye no ken hoo lassies git weans?' upcastit Allison.

'Winchin,' May bangt back.

'Aye, bit dae ye ken the ins an oots o it?'

'A bit.'

'Spill it then.'

'Well, its goat somethin tae dae wi wrappin roon each ither awfy close... an kissin for ages... an taken yer claes aff... Ah've nivver done that... an moanin an breathin lood. Ann Weir says if ye open yer mooth when yer kissin ye kin git pregnant... yeuch... wha wid waant tae dae that?'

Allison squecht. 'If that gies ye the boak, git this roon yer lugs... Ye dinnae ken the hauf o it... Oor Beth telt me the hale thing... bit she gittered oan aboot no blawin it aw aboot the place... she said ma mither wid hae kittens if she kent she'd telt me...'

'Allison, are ye ever gaun tae tell *me?*'

'...ay bit ye hae tae *sweir* ye'll no tell anither livin sowl.'

'Aw richt... Ah sweir.'

May hung oantae ilka ward that clasht fae Allison's mooth. Yince or twice there wis a bit o argy bargy ower whit wur the richt names fur boady pairts they'd haurly ivver clapt een oan: whit Allison cried a laddie's 'wee man' May cawed a 'wullie'.

'Ma grannie caws it *graith...*' said May.

'Graith?'

'Aye... when oany oor boays ur footerin aboot in thur troosers ma grannie shouts, *"lea yer graith alane or ye'll go blin"...*'

Allison began tae lauch an May jined in til they were baith rowin aboot, haudin their sides an skirlin lik a pair o bubbly-joaks.

'Onywey... hoo kin they... hoo kin they... git that... inside ye?' speirt May, wipin the tears fae her een, an thinkin o the wee, saft, pink, shrivelt things that dwaiblt atween the legs o her three brithers.

'A dinnae ken withir tae believe this, May... bit Beth says that aw the time yer kissin an cuddlin a laddie, his wee man is growin bigger... an boukit... tae its the size o a spurtle...'

May's een wur reelin. 'Is your Beth richt in the heid?'

'Ah ken... a thocht that masel... but she sweirs it's richt... an she's goat twa weans... she should ken.'

'An how kin that gie ye a wean?' went oan May, her shoothers shooglin.

'Ah'm no goannae tell ye if ye keep lauchin ivvry time a say su'thin.'

'Aw richt... oan ye go.'

'Well, Beth says the lassie pairts her legs an the laddie pits his wee man...'

'Which is a *big* man bi noo...' May chimed in.

'Aye... wid ye be quate!...'

As Allison explained aboot white snottery stuff an seed being plantit, the wind drapt aw o a sudden, lea'in wee flechterin eddies gaun naewhere.

'Naw. Ah couldnae dae that... diz yer sister like dain it?' said May.

'She nivver said an Ah nivver askt... bit... ah've decidit no tae hae ony weans... or git mairrit... wid *you*?'

'No efter whit ye've jist telt me... it sounds affy sair! Bit whit wid we dae?... Bide wi wur mithers aw oor days?... Ye kin only git a hoose if ye're mairrit.'

Allison thocht a bit, chawin oan a new bit o grass. 'Miss Forrest's no mairrit... she bides in that big hoose wi her twa sisters... they're no mairrit either... she wis tellin us wan day in English... tae set oor sights high... git oot o this place... even fur a year or twa efter we lea skuil. She telt us aboot weemin that hae done great things... Ah cannae mind their names... Ah think yin wis cawed Mary Sommerville... an Elsie Inglis. Wan wis a great scientist an the ither hud tae dae wi maakin weemmin hae weans easier... *"easing the lot of expectant mothers"* wis whit she said.'

'An they *awfy likely spoke ez posh ez Miss Forrest,"* said May, wi a skeich getherin in o her lips.

An the licht wis gaun, lik nicht cam early, as thick, heavy-hertit clouds thronged in fae the West. Sae keen they wur, neither lassie hud sklent at the sky, noo sae mirky wi a thin scad ower Taplaw. Aw at yince, they felt the hairs staun up oan their airms, legs, an faces, heard the brattle an rout o thunner an then the hoat plash as the clouds lit go their ain seed. In the twa-three saicints it took them tae rise oan their pegs they were drookit an yelpin. Allison liftit up her face, een shut an mooth yawin, tae catch the waarm blash, littin it rin doon her thrapple, greedy as a tinkler gaitherin gowd. May stertit tae birl, slow an lithe, weavin her airms abin her heid, feelin the waarm watter reem ower her airms, her neck, her legs; felt it sine her hair, her foosty claes.

'Race ye tae the ither en!' bawled Allison ower the soun o the thunner.

An oaf they stertit; lang leish legs slashin through the grass, airms oot-streecht, heids back an hair plaistert tae their necks. Oan an oan they skelpt, scrauchin as they whuppt ower doakies an boolders. Allison reacht the ither side first. As she birled roon, May whammed richt intae her an near backt her intae the hedge ahint. They grippt each ither, baith missin a fit oan the gutterie grun. Fur a saicint or twa, they dottert this wey an that, til they keeled ower, each haudin oantae the ither. The rain hud near gien ower, bit the grun they had landit oan wis fast turnin intae a new burn. Rid-faced an hechlin, they lay wi their airms aroon each ither, the watter soomin by them. It wis a guid few meenits afore they wur laucht oot, wi jist an occasional sob threatnin tae stert them aff again.

'It's great huvin you fur a pal,' said Allison as she kissed May oan the cheek.

'Aye... intit,' cam back May, peerin hard at Allison's saft rid lips. She touched the ither lassie's cheek wi her ain an sniffed, sayin, 'Ah think we're lyin in a pile o auld coo shite.'

'Luk at whit's comin,' said May in a low saft voice.

'Ah see them...'

Jacky Doyle, Samuel Parker an Jacky's da's whippet hud jist cam intae view at the end o the lane. Samuel hud a big stick that he was lashin the hedges wi, sendin up sprays o watter drapplets. May an Allison hud sined the dung oot o their hair an claes in a troch-stane an were oan their wey hame, airms linkt and their baffies squelchin in perfik unison. They turnt their heids tae yin anither, pretendin tae be deep in talk. Jacky Doyle's face wis gettin rosier bi the meenit, mindin how he'd missed his chance last nicht. He wis jist imaginin whit he wid say the next time he got May oan her ain, when they aw drew level wi each ither. His ee took in the deep chestnut sheen o her wet hair an the shadda o her nipples through the still-damp blouse. He opent his mooth tae say somethin an then shut it again as May lookt him straucht in the ee. It wisnae a freenly look, he thocht; no feart exactly, but no freenly either. He yanked the dug's lead as the whippet lunged fur Allison, sniffin lik mad. Nane o them spoke as they passed each ither. May kent whit the look in Jacky's een meant, an inside her heid she heard hersel think 'Ye're too late, Jacky Doyle, too late.'

Allison wis gaun ower in her heid whit she wid say tae her mither. It was aye the same... *yer late... whaur wur ye?... wur ye talkin tae ony laddies?...* This yince she wid be able tae tell the hale truth. She wid tell her mither no tae fash – she'd been wi May aw the time an they nivver spoke tae ony laddies.

Gordon Meade

THREE FISHGUTTERS
after John Bellany

The sea has eroded each one differently,
In her own peculiar way. She has drowned
Each one's future perfectly, completely

Submerged them, in hers. They stand above
A slab of fish, their hands trembling
Nervously, their knife blades glistening

In the artificial light. They are keen
To begin her work of disembowelling; of her
Children, of each other, of our lives.

ANSWERING THE ANCHOR

In the old days, herring were found by sight.
On late summer nights, a fisherman would strike
The boat's gunwale with the anchor shank. The sound,
Through water, made the herring start, and created

An incandescent flash. They called it 'burning',
And said the herring were 'answering the anchor'.
Tonight, guided only by the sound of our voices,
Let's find ourselves and rise to the bite. Let's burn
For each other, and answer the anchor of love.

Iain Mills

MOTOR CITY

The hum and clatter of the line, the clash of gear-box casings banging into place, screamed conversations between men half-deafened by years of car plant cacophony.

'...tae Stubbs... night... Eddie...'

Fill in the gaps and make a conversation, lip-reading an advantage. You got good at it, given time.

Afterwards crossing the car park, frost settling on the tarmac and industrial hiss still filling our ears.

'Sure – pick us up at seven? Coupla beers first?'

A quick scrub at the sink then a shave, steam from the geyser clouding the mirror, razor rasping across bristles, tingling feeling in the stomach. All part of the ritual. Get yer tea down as quick as you can, yer Maw telling you tae take yer time. The last bit of bread folded over and stuffed in your mouth as the toot from Davie's car ricochets around the tenements. Billy's got his tape recorder in the back seat: the Isley Brothers. 'This Old Heart of Mine' turning Paisley into downtown Detroit. We knew every word, all of us.

'Eddie says he'll get us in Kennedy's.'

Tooting at the girls we pass, rubbing our sleeves on steamed up windows so we can get a better look; willing Davie's rust-bucket Hillman tae get us there.

'Want us tae pit our feet through the flair an push Davie?'

'Fuck off. Yeez want tae walk?'

Kennedy's first.

'Three pintsa heavy, packet a twenty Regal.'

'Where y'offtae the night lads?'

'Stubbs.'

'Work in the morning?'

'Mibby.'

Thinking of Stubbs.

'Eddie man, whit ye for? Lager Shandy? Ye a poof?'

'Who is the DJ the night?'

Down in the basement, just off Causeyside. Eight till late – with the best Motown sounds this side of the Atlantic. No place like it, pure 22-carat gold. 'Stubbs'? Yeah, lotsa people asked that. Named after Levi Stubbs, god-like singer wi the Four Tops.

'Ye know whit Ah think?' One of Eddie's theories on the way. 'It's the rhythm. The factory. The rhythm of the machines. The rhythm of the work.'

'What is?'

'Like Detroit. They invented Motown. They've got these giant car plants... Ford... Chrysler...'

'Whit ye on about Eddie?'

'It's like the rhythm o the factory an the rhythm o the music – it's the same. That's why they like it an we like it tae.'

'Shite.'

'Paisley's Scotland's Detroit. Motown UK. The same work an the same music.'

'Shite. It's just good music. The best.'

It was a good theory though. Lasted all the way from Kennedy's tae Stubbs.

Cropped bouncers frisking us, even though they know us:

'Stop it Wullie, ye know Ah like it.' Same line every time.

Then down the stairs. One at a time. Real slow, savouring the glorious mix of heat, sweat and beautiful sounds rising from the basement, teasing ourselves by lingering on the stairs. Through the doors, eyes adjusting to the dark as we worked our way round the edge past the dancers, 'Jimmy Mack' pulsing from the speakers an us singin along. Girls with panstick an mascara swivelling in front of us, familiar faces from other Tuesdays. Bottles of coke frae the bar topped up wi vodka in the toilets. Even in there the pounding bass notes found yer rib cage: 'Uptight', 'Loving You is sweeter than ever', 'Ain't too proud to beg'. In the toilet there's this guy we've never met before an he's givin us Berry Gordy's life history an tellin us how a girl he knows once met Marvin Gaye backstage in Manchester. Wow. Ben Sherman shirts an Sta Press trousers worn *just* right. Coupla guys wi pills. Stubbs on a Tuesday. Drinkin, sweatin, dancin an singin an dancin. Struttin tae Marvin then it's Smokey an 'Tracks of my tears' an nuzzlin girls' necks as we move real slow, tasting their perfume an feeling them move against us. Three girls on the far side doin some new dance an lookin real good. Nobody looks at their watches – time doesn't matter any more. It's 1968, we've money in our pockets an the best music in the world's pourin out the speakers an that's all that counts. A Curtis Mayfield import...

We're over at the bar gettin some more cokes an some o the Johnstone crowd are in. 'Reach Out' comes on an one of them shouts 'No' mair o that Four Tops shite – geez the Temptations.'

Ah looks at Davie. He looks at Billy. Eddie looks at the Johnstone boys.

'Am Ah hearin things?' says Davie.

Eddie goes it alone: 'Whit *you* on aboot?'

'There's no' enough Temptations here – it's aw that Four Tops crap. That's no' real Motown – jist Pop, nae soul...'

'Listen,' says Eddie, 'that's the most brilliant sound in the world, an Levi Stubbs has *the* greatest Motown voice, the saddest, most beautiful...'

'Levi Stubbs? Couldnae sing his way oot a paper bag. If him an David Ruffin went ten roons – singin like – ther's only gonna be wan winner.'

'Ruffin? No' in the same league...'

The music dies an the Johnstone boy bawls out 'Geez Get Ready,' but it's more Smokey.

'C'mon Eddie,' says Billy, 'he's no' worth botherin aboot.'

Cigarette smoke hazed around the speakers. It was hot – even the walls were runnin wi sweat.

'An that's another thing,' says the Johnstone boy, turnin tae us, 'See thae Four Tops words – aw that "Sugar pie honeybunch" shite – Ah cannae...'

He didnae get a chance tae finish his sentence: Eddie was at him an everyone else piled in. Lassies screamin, bottles flyin... At least wi the drink ye don' feel the punches the same... Then the bouncers are wadin in, no' takin ony prisoners. 'Tears of a Clown' still playin, but it's the last record for us. Decent guys though, the bouncers – jist threw us oot – nae polis or nuthin...

Standin in the street shoutin after the Johnstone boys. They're gettin off their mark. Billy sends a bottle after them, shoutin 'That's wan fur Levi,' then it's aw quiet.

'Think we'll get back in?'

'Nae chance.'

We wandered off down the lane.

'Time's it?' My watch had gone.

We turned the corner and I could see the clock face on the Town Hall: 1.15. Felt earlier.

'Wanna go for a run? Listen tae some music?'

Back into Orchard Street and Davie's car. Someone had

stolen his tape recorder. All his cassettes as well. They were worth more than the car!

Driving back, deserted streets.

'Watch for the polis, boys.'

'An whit if we see them Davie?'

'Slow down.'

'Yer no' even daein thirty Davie – this thing couldnae speed goin' doonhill wi a gale behind it!'

'Ye'll no be sayin that next week. Ah've sneaked enough parts oot the work tae practically build a new engine.'

'Sure Davie!'

'Youse aw gawn in in the mornin?'

All except Billy...

Then in the morning. Standing at the line, twirlin a spanner an tryin tae look busy; movin ma jaw from side tae side tae see how much it hurts; wonderin how soon Ah can nip out tae the toilet for a smoke...

An then Ah hears it. It's no' a noise – it's a rhythm. Man, machinery an tools blendin together in a throbbin Motown beat.

For once Eddie was right.

William Neill

Thrie Sonnets frae Giuseppe Belli (1791-1861)

FAUR BEN THE DAY, SCUNNER THE MORN
(Well in today, cause of disgust tomorrow)

Don Marco wes convickit o adulterie	
bein fund atour the dochters o Severio.	found across, daughters
'I'm geyan shair that yon's no true ava,'	very sure, indeed
the Paip said, shrivin him frae aa sculdud-	
derie.	sexual antics

He pauchled siller, med a richt cletter tae	swindled money, scandal
he tuk a lenn o a guid wheen o fowk.	took advantage, large number
'A man lik him wad shairlie no begowk	surely not deceive
onibodie,' said the Paip an lat him gae.	

At the hinner enn, a sauntlie spy tellt aa;	finally, saintly, last night
gied a wee souch or twa o the latest dirt:	whisper
'Marco, yir Hauliness, is a Jacobin.'	

An bein duntit whaur it maistlie hurt,	struck
His Hauliness, nae shuiner said than duin,	
damned him athoot due process o the laa.	without

Sonetto 1275

THE ILL-MAINNERT PAUPER

D'ye mynd ava yon blissid puir young tink   remember at all, tramp
wha's nichtlie ludgin wes ablo the stair   lodging in below
o the count cardinal's pailace ower thare   palace
as if it wes an orra publick bink?   common public bench

Gin ye'd draa back a bittock dinnae think   little bit
ye shawed a want o mense; when he wad
                       bare   lack of sense
his airse ablo the hap, ye maun be shair   horse-blanket, arse
yir neb wad fairlie runkle et the stink.   nose, wrinkle

An by his Excellency's dure, ye'll gree,   door, agree
ti boak his ugsome slitters doun ablo –   vomit, horrid, slavers
jist nestiness! An shairlie he wes dowff,   daft

richt in the verra presence thare ti *dee*
as gin he beddit in some orra howff.   as if, common hovel
A want aa respeck thare, wes thare no?

         Sonetto 2168

THE MUGS AN THE MERCAT

I'm shair ye'll ken that aa yon mercat-cairts   market-carts
wi cribs o chookies, eggs in muckle rips   coops of hens, large baskets
are gaun for sale, but *ye* maun sook yir
                    lips –   suck
thir's no for paupers but for weill-daein
                    airts.   these, well-to-do places

An no for us the chance o muckle bings   great piles
o gustie sunkets. We maun stainch oor need   tasty morsels, staunch
wi twa-thrie syboes an a crust o breid   two or three spring onions
the day, the morn, stairvin on siclike things.   today, tomorrow, suchlike

Cardinals an friars, hures an priests,   whores
lairds, weill-aff clerks an mercat-kings
ti siccan tastie maits can help thaimsels.   such, meats

Thae seiven-fault sinners: orra beists   common
jist like the puir; but free ti glog sich things   gulp down
while we maun be contentit wi the smells.

Sonetto 1001

Patricia Nic Fhionghain

AM BEURLA

Cluinnidh mi a guth cho binn
a'pògadh timchioll mo chluasan
's tarraingidh i mi air dannsa
Leis na gàirdeanan theann
Ach thana pògan fuar
Mar deigh air barr na geige
nuair a thigeas an geamhradh bho thuath.

Cumaidh i air làimh mi
's falbhaidh sinn air chuairt
Ach cha ghreimich i mi
An uair a thuiteas mi sìos
a'bualadh an talamh chruaidh.

Seinnidh i òrain
Coltach mar an smeòrach
Milis mar an t-seun
a tha teannachadh d'inntinn
Ach brisidh an guth mìl
'S cha bhi ann ach sgread
Cho searbh 's gun cuir e
deòir air m'aodainn.

Dannsaidh i mar duilleagan
air a'ghaoith
'S theid mise còmhla rithe
Air ruidhle a theideas mu chuairt
mar rothan
Ach seididh a h-anail cho reòite
'S cuiridh i na corragan fuar
timchioll air m'amhaich.

Bheiridh i dhomhsa na duaisean
Mar ghaol 's sin leat
'S cumaidh i greim orm
Ach cha leig i mi air falbh.

Cha chaill mi m'anam
leis an t-searbhant bhochd eile
'S i feitheamh air an cùlaibh
A'fulaing 's air a bualadh
gus an till na gaisgich,
Air ais gu an t-suirighe.

IN ENGLISH

I hear her voice so sweet
kissing my ears
enticing me to dance
With her strong arms
But the kisses are cold
Like ice on the branches
When the winter comes from north.

She will hold me by my hand
And we will walk
But she won't hold me
When I fall
Hitting the hard ground.

She will sing a song
like the thrush
A sweet charm
That hypnotises your mind
But the sweet voice will break
Leaving nothing but a shriek
So bitter that it leaves
Tears on my face.

She will dance
Like the leaves on the wind
And I will go with her
On a reel
Which will go round like a wheel
But her breath will blow so cold
And she will place her cold fingers
Around my neck.

She will give me gifts
Like love and such things
She will hold me
But she won't let me leave.

I will not lose my soul
With the other poor servant
Waiting at the rear
Suffering and abused.
Until the heroes finally return
To the challenge.

D.G. O'Donnell

THE IMPLACABLE

Unless my memory plays me false,
It fell out one night at the end of the year,
A stormy night, many years ago,
As I sat in a bar on the Rue Favorites.
The rain was being lashed along the street
And hurtled off of gable ends,
Windblown in the night air, deep and far
And brattling the panes of the little bar.
Visible through the unpebbled upper section
Of the window, the inn house sign
Swung and scraped in the wind,
And the door was cuffed from time to time
By squalls that had lost their sense of direction.

The racks of glasses winked and shone,
Each a reflection, miniature and discreet,
Of the dull flare of the lamps that were on
In the wall-brackets, and the curate lolled
Over the polished counter, for the shop
Was quiet as the grave, and just as cold.
He rubbed his palms for heat
And presented his backside to the fire,
But conversation was a social grace
He never seemed to have acquired;
Although I was the only other living soul
In the place, he stayed as dumb as a prop.
I sat behind a glass of spirituous amber
And blew rings of smoke at the lights,
And listened to the death throes of December
Out there as the year took flight.

The door crashed open and the wind blew in
A man with his collar up, soaked and frozen.
Certainly he looked as if he'd been battered
By time and the elements; his clothes and
His shoes, though not exactly tattered,
Had seen much better days.

But then, who hasn't? He carried a case,
Equally bashed about and closed
By two belts around its girth.
He took out a hanky and wiped his face
And spectacles, unbelted his coat,
Unrolled his muffler from around his throat,
And ordered – oh, snake-oil of some description.
He carried the summary of all our woes
In his deeply-lined features.
If it hadn't been for me, he might have been
The loneliest man on God's wide earth,
Standing there, sipping his Teachers
And looking like he got it four times a day,
Instead of meals, and on prescription.

Like certain predatory creatures, the ones that
Home in upon a victim's anxious scent,
He knew that the last thing I wanted was company,
But that was not at all what he meant
For me that night, and he brought the drink
Over to where I sat. I saw he had a limp
And the look of a traveller – or a man from the coast.
He let his weary body sink
Into the faded plush of the seat.
He seemed tired of it all, but no more than most,
I don't suppose. I looked at my feet
Unsocially, and savoured the bite of my smoke,
Till his voice, strangely soft for such a man,
Made me lift my head and look when he spoke.

He said, not asked, 'You want to know
What's in the case. Naturally. You do.'

'No, I don't,' I said, and averted my face.
'Whatever you're selling, I want none.'

He reached out a skinny hand to my arm
Then smiled and nodded knowingly, said, 'Son,
You do. But don't worry. It'll do you no harm.'

He took a tin from the pocket of his coat
And teased a few threads from a lump of shag,
Laid them out carefully on a Rizla green,
Rolled it and ran the tip of his tongue
Around the gummed edge. 'Bad for the lungs,'
He said and he smiled and lit his fag.

My curiosity was piqued, I have to admit.
I don't think I have ever before seen
Anyone like him. And he talked double Dutch.
– I wasn't sure then and I'm not sure now
Just what it was. He wasn't all there,
That's for sure; something didn't fit;
Not to mince words, the bastard was touched.
But, in spite of my earlier insouciant air,
I had to find out somehow, now,
Whatever it was he had in there.

'Okay, I give in,' says I. 'What's in the case?'

He twitched his nose, picked a hair
Or baccy from his lip and thought for a while.
Then he said, 'You are, son.'

                              – He must a seen my face,
For he patted my arm very nicely and smiled,
Trying his best to reassure me calmly:

'I know what you think – it's no surprise –
But you can take it from me – I'm not balmy.'

'No, not hellish much.'
                              He pushed up his glasses
On his nose and said, with a worn-out sigh,
'Don't be like that. I cancelled my classes
To get here tonight. Here, have a look.'

He opened the case and took out three books,
Hardbacked notebooks, all with my name:
Volume One, Childhood; Volume Two, Youth;
Volume Three, Adulthood.

'This is your life,
– You know the TV programme? Well, just the same,
But in this case every single word is the truth.'

'Gimme them here.'
                              'Ah, no, not so fast.
You give me a tenner and you can have all three.
I'm sure they're more use to you than to me –
It's your whole life here, first to last.'

'A tenner? Now I know that you're cracked.'

'Ah, well. What a shame – it's a pity about that.
Really it is.' And he put one back, shut the lid.
Then he held up the other two books once again.
'Okay, you can have these for – say, twenty quid,
If you like,' he said.
                              I goes, 'Hey, talk sense,'
I says, 'you're going from bad to worse.'

He never turned a hair,
But shook his head like a tolerant nurse
With a patient whose wanderings have got more intense.

'Okay,' he sighed, and replaced a book.
'I hate to see you beat yourself. Look,
This one here' – he held it up – 'is the best
And it's three times as valuable as the rest.
Childhood's back in the case, so's Youth –
Would have been nice to be able to see them again
But you made your choice and that's up to you.
Now let me warn you before you do
Anything you're going to end up regretting:
You ought to grab Adulthood with both hands.
I'll let you have it for fifty. How's that?
It'll tell you a few things, old and new,
Things you should know. And not be forgetting.
Five big tenners and it's yours. There's a deal.

What do you say?'
                    I let him know how I feel
In no uncertain terms. He sighed and said,

'Some folk never learn; they spurn every chance.'

He ruffled through the book and tore out a page.
He put the third book in the case, drained his glass,
Thrust the torn sheet on the table, and with a last
'You could have done well – you insisted on losing'
Left the bar to the barman and me and my boozing
And slipped away without a backward glance.

I watched as the doors closed on the figure,
Looked at the barman and shook my head with a snigger.
Then I picked up the page and I read.

The page was headed with that day's date
And went on to summarise the events of my day,
Ending with this: *In the evening he met*
An eccentric in a bar who tried to sell
Him the entire and complete analysis of his life,
But he refused the chance scornfully
And it cuts like a knife.

Well, I up out that chair and I out through the doors …
But there wasn't a sign of him out on the street;
Just the signpost swinging crazily in the wind
And the rain washing puddles of lights round my feet.

Well now, all that's a long time ago,
And I've never seen him again. If I did, I'd spend
Any God's amount to have those books.
But one thing nags at me time and again:
Did he tear that page out at the start or the end?

And how many pages remained?

Donny O'Rourke

DEAR ANDREW McGREGOR

I've become my mum –
wireless on all morning
not Wogan or Clyde
for me but Radio Three
and you Andrew McGregor,
Whose name I growl
with its gritty, rolling, Rob Roy
'Rs' a great big gruff,
hairy and heroic name,
trailing gravel and burrs –
though you yourself have mild
Tony Blair style vowels and Home
Counties headnotes: a high
nuzzling whinny that seems
to say 'Nanny, can I
have a sugar lump?'
I'd give you a sugar lump:
I'd give you two! Andrew
are you medium height,
slight, thinning in your thirties,
I know you cycle in;
you told me. Bet it's not
a mountain bike. Bet you!
I used to get up with you
at seven; now we both start
at the crack of six.
Dear Andrew, this is not
some foolish fad of mine.
My dial's spinning!
My aerial's up!
If I've guessed right about
you, send me a sign:
make your third piece on
Thursday, the misterioso
movement from Furtwangler's
pre-war recording of
Bruckner's symphony number nine.

THE WAIST BAND

If you don't stop soon
you'll end up gross and penitent
like some wire jawed sack of slurry
with a stapled gut
spilling it on the tea-time talk shows
how, 'people of size'
are gonna sue the car manufacturers
the airlines, the funeral parlours
for cutting it fine –
the right to be roomy
and twenty odd stone
in a Corvette
on a Boeing
in a glass topped
magenta catafalque
in quaking polyester
is the right to be a fat bastard
a grazer on grease
a waddling gullet
frankly a glutton
if one may resort to theology

the game's up Porky

your mirror is telling you
the scales are telling you
between mouthfuls of cheeseburger
Elves in nappies is telling you
everything is telling you

now go ask the fridge

RESORT

Long before I butterfingered your lucky heirloom tumbler
we were more or less washed up but that night:

the warning light definitely came on while we pan
and shovelled shards of leaded Irish crystal

in the scullery cum kitchenette of the coup
you'd rented to be closer. Clammy nights

of fervent, futile fucking, our cum cries ever
more lunatically raucous until both of us

were barking. Our brave faces deserved medals.
We grinned but couldn't bear it, still tried

gamely one more time, what the hell, a doughty
short lived stab at couples in a heat wavering

Welsh resort at the fullest top-most tip
of what ought to have been our season. You were

perfect then, I priapic in my prime that peachy
last weekend, two, too hot days between ripe and rotten.

THE LOVE SONG OF DANIEL O'BESE

First my gone gaunt love made my weight
an ultima-tum; and then a casius belly.

Richard Price

THE HIGH ROAD: PART ONE

The stepladder makes an A
in the ABC for the child
kickstarting its heart
in a woman called Jack.
The bedroom's been licked
with Dulux Magnolia Silk
and that's the Fabers cleared
for the new cot beside us.

Emulsion's in our throats,
the glossed windowsills
pant in the after-snow rain.
Herman M. Scopes
for ICI Paints, says:
Thank you for writing to me
on the subject of the effects
of CFCs on the ozone layer.
All of us here and our families
share your concern
for the environment...

'Magic rug from Selfridges,'
I find myself commanding,
'I've slid the secondary glazing
out its lip,
now kill the rain
and take us up.'

We feel the drop,
then
        the
                compensating.

We're up above
the low maintenance shrubbery.
We're up above
the black nacreous puddlery!
We're up above
the carpark and its wrecks:
a plugless old fax,
the Sierra on bricks,
a broken-up desk.

It's me who speaks:

'Carpet, skim each ledge,
each cold-sweat pane of glass,
each window's latch.
Be a busybody chopper!
Buzz the football pennants,
that waterlogged jotter,
that LibDem patch.

'Fly further – past
the spreadsheet light
of the home accountant,
past a dripping shirt
all wilt by the curtains,
past the Venetians
skewed to a fan.

'Fly by that bong,
by that unkempt spliff,

'fly by
the explicit amaryllis,
the fleshy cactus,
the red pout
of a Fairy Liquid,

'fly by
diaried pills in foil,
by cream and gel,
by slenderly-bottled oils,

'by all the peopleness
of people's sills.

'Go deeper still –'

'Honourable floor covering,
heed my call,'
Jack interjects,
'Forget those active bedrooms,
the private and the illicit:
out no-one to celebrate
my husband celebrating.

Did you both forget
the acrid starter-flats
crammed with itching children?
the de-clawed cat's
cloying owner?
forget nextdoor?
his late-stage melanoma?

'Carpet, walk all over
no-one.
Give just-making-do's
tense privacy
one last freedom.
Look to who
looks after you,
and to your own label's legend:
People's soles are my burden,
my mission is to soften
gravity,
to bear felicity and indiscretion;
only dry clean.

'Mean what that means,
or it's a spin with the 'Heavy Soileds'
when we touch base again.

'And Richard, a buzzing helicopter?
Your highness should know better!
I'd be stretching it, to say the least,
to claim we're riding
a 'woven flying dhow',
but you think you're the RAF
or in Apocalypse Now.

'I don't make it up,
say this morning's a Night and it's Arabian:
it's as plain as day (and the price)
this mat is not a Persian.
So when you're setting out
to set this down
keep to the facts and don't defile it:
your licence is a writer's
not a bomber pilot's.'

HILLMAN AVENGER

When we raise a new cross on Barochan Hill
it will not be a Cross. To serve us instead
we'll haul up a wreck from Linwood's old works,
pull a car out a Renfrew scrappy.

Imagine the pullies, the drive up the field,
the event. We'll rub its nose in the plinth, force
all its doors aghast. We'll build to last that dive
only ad cars pull themselves out of.

Dilys Rose

CONSIDER YOURSELF KISSED

The blue hydrangeas are dotted around the tables; squat, chubby blossoms in their little cellophane skirts; scentless and showy, not my type of flower at all. Too sturdy, regular, too sure of itself. Bougainvillea I like; the delicate, flimsy blooms have a depth, a passion to them. There is no depth to hydrangeas. They are a flat, waxy reliable blue, like railing paint.

I can't talk about flowers to Gleason though I can talk about railings. Gleason has been putting up railings everywhere, even on the balcony, making our new apartment secure. I told him crown-of-thorns works better than any railing for keeping thieves at bay but Gleason believes man's inventions are superior to nature. Besides, he likes a job to be done and that's it, finished. No upkeep. No maintenance. Clean cut. Something definite, final and railings don't need cutting back like crown-of-thorns.

But these new railings we have need paint. I can't live my life behind black bars, even if they're special fancy ironwork with loops and curlicues. Black railings are never pretty, I tell Gleason, and what is life worth if your home is a prison? He says,

– If you don't like the black, I'll paint them blue, so when you stand on the tiled balcony and look out, all you'll notice is the sky.

Gleason believes in working from the inside out, so while he was taking care of the bedroom bolts and bars on the bathroom windows – which is too small for even a child thief to squeeze through – I decided to try some crown-of-thorns at street level. Not even the craziest housebreaker would try to cross my hedge; beneath the red bracts lurks a more vicious deterrent than barbed wire. The problem now is keeping the hedge under control; it has grown, like everything does here, fast and furious, sprawling over the pathway. Tonight, on the way out, I gashed my knee on my own protection system. Blood spattered my dancing shoes. I was lucky not to ruin my new dress.

All the way along the street I could hear the music and the cars pulling up and skidding on the dry earth around the gymnasium. The air is so sweet tonight, intoxicating, like the memory of a caress. Night scents are always the sweetest, though often they're produced by plain plants. I would have liked to take my time, to enjoy the coolness, inhale slowly and deeply, savour the air but I was late. A sharp little pain burned in my chest as I hurried along. The dance must already be in full swing and all too soon it would be over.

I am very happy with Gleason but there are times when I feel… shut in. Tonight, as I sped along the seams of the dress which I was rushing like mad to finish, because nothing fits since the last time I went dancing, he hovered on the balcony. He hovered and fussed with his elaborate system of locks and bolts. Sometimes the extra security makes me feel insecure. Put up a fence, you invite a stranger to break it down. Think about something all the time, it's going to happen.

– Even thieves take vacation, I say. Go ahead without me. I'll join you soon. Consider yourself kissed.

His fussing distracted me, slowed me down and made me cross.

I don't want to be cross with Gleason. He is thinking only of the best for us and I know something has to be done. There have been nights when I too have lain awake, unable to identify a sound amongst the frogs hammering on the pond, the cicadas drilling holes in the darkness, banana palms snapping under the weight of their fruit – there are a score of sounds that I could name – nights when I was convinced I could hear papery whispers and the dull pad of bare feet, nights when I lay still as a lizard, barely breathing.

But mostly, knowing that Gleason is there in the bed beside me, I can give myself up to the luxury of sleep, assured that nothing can disturb us, nothing leap out of the darkness. And even if it did, it wouldn't get through Gleason's lines of defence, no I am well protected.

How pretty the students look in their perky white suits, berets perched on their heads. Gleason is supervisor to twenty student teachers, girls with little ambition other than to find a husband, soon. When you're paid less than a cleaner you don't see teaching as a long term vocation. Their energy and enthusiasm will be sapped from them slowly but surely, no, cleaning is a more rewarding occupation. You see results, make people happy, in a small way. A teacher encounters too much failure. I know.

When I met Seph – and married him almost immediately – I was a tired-out teacher. Not that marriage improved my own circumstances in any practical way. *Husband* is not a correct description of what Seph was to me. People say love is about chemistry, well, Seph and I had the kind of chemistry which mostly made explosions. By ourselves we might have been two stable substances but together, pfftt – blue flashes and a smell of burning.

So many people are up dancing that there are plenty empty tables near the floor. I sit at one and wait for Gleason to finish his social duties and find me. He is congratulating his students for passing their exams and wishing them luck for the future. In his professional role, he is so relaxed, so expansive, a man at ease with the world, and himself. I note the girls who kiss him twice and those who kiss him three times as he takes his leave from them, leisurely, so leisurely, to join his new wife. I pay particular attention to the three-kiss girls; two of them. For one it's a stagey affectation, a habit picked up from the television. The other I'm not so sure. Less flourish. More intensity. Is it a hint that she's available or is she too just following a trashy fashion? The three-kiss habit is tricky. It's the accompanying gestures, the flutter of an eyebrow, the clasp of hands, list of the body that you have to pay attention to. With the second three-kiss girl, Gleason's embrace is distinctly more than a grazing of cheeks. I crinkle the hydrangea's cellophane skirt. Do I care about this?

The waiter comes over to my table and sweeps the empty plastic beer cups on to the concrete floor – this is the worst thing about the new building regulations – how can anyone dance on concrete? A dead floor, still, even over concrete it is possible, with the right partner, to feel weightless...

The fashion is shorts and mini skirts again this year, nothing with a swing to it, nothing which gives itself to the music. But I like watching the dancers, the showy and the shy, the graceful and oddly awkward, complete strangers, couples who have been too close for too long, those lit up by love or dulled by dis-appointment. I know most of the people here. When you're the only hairdresser in town, you get to know a lot of people. In a small way, of course. And they know me. In a small way.

Gleason has worked through the sailor-suited girls to my table. He's got a swagger on him as he says, in his old-fashioned but lovable way:

– Here I am, dear, to take care of you.

Anywhere other than a dance floor and I'd be more than happy but not here, not now. The dance floor is not at all the place for Gleason to take care of me. Though I didn't come here just to spectate, though I'm itching to move with the music, my foot stops tapping, my bones set into a rigid wall against the beat.

If somebody would just come and join us, interrupt us, detain us at the table, let us be the happy new couple that we are. But his girls have turned back to their boyfriends, Gleason is standing over me, offering his arm, his secure, protective arm. I smooth down my dress and let him lead me on to the floor.

Gleason presses his cheek against mine. His breath is hot and enthusiastic. He is a noisy breather, even when he is not exerting himself. That and the teeth sucking, I don't like. Nor the way he rolls up his vest when it's hot, to air his belly. I don't mind his bigness, I'm no string bean myself, but why draw attention to your fondness for beer? But these are silly things and tonight Gleason's not slobbing around in a vest, no, he's spruced up, dapper in black trousers and blue dress shirt, tucked into his belt. I should be, *would* be proud of him, anywhere but on the dance floor.

Gleason whirls me round the room, fast, too fast, racing the beat, unable to hear the way it pulls back, hesitates, changes direction, tone, missing all the small twists and turns which make the tune beautiful, seductive. It's disappointing in a man so particular about the details when it comes to railings and pathways. But music, to Gleason, is only a pattern of notes. As he is counting out five, six, seven, eight into my ear, Seph and his new girlfriend brush past us and I lose the rhythm entirely.

Seph; I don't want Seph and he doesn't want me. We both knew this, felt it long before we were able to put it into words, before we were able, finally, to part. And now we have our separate, better lives.

Gleason and I have our differences but they are easy differences – like about the railings – they can be smoothed out, or covered up and ignored. Gleason and I do not share big, painful differences, which is why we have such a secure arrangement, why we are a good partnership.

– Maybe we should sit down, I say, after the third dance in a row.

My dress is crushed to a rag where his hands have been, in

spite of the good fabric. Seph's hands never left a mark on my dresses.

– But you love dancing.

– Let's get a beer.

– But you don't like beer. And they're playing samba. You love samba.

– I'm thirsty, Gleason.

– Didn't you have wine earlier?

I call the waiter, order beer and sit down. Gleason sits down too, after wiping some crumbs off his seat. He is about to lecture me on the dangers of mixing grape and grain when he sees the gash on my leg. It looks quite dramatic when the flashing stage lights hit it, a dark zig-zag.

– Whatever happened?

It's nothing, but it gives me an excuse to sit out the samba. I explain about the crown-of-thorns and straight away Gleason's fear of calamity overwhelms him.

There's something toxic in the thorns, he thinks, highly toxic. To be on the safe side, I should really have a tetanus injection, though it's an hour's drive to the hospital, a long wait is inevitable, it's very late already, and maybe, all things considered, it might be better to go home and dab on some arnica – Gleason believes this plant cures everything from backache to warts – and review the situation in the morning. One thing is certain, the crown-of-thorns will have to go. First thing in the morning. If it can't be dug up, it'll be burnt. After the recent drought, it will go up like a torch. But if the crown-of-thorns is removed, there will be inadequate security and didn't I see now that it would have been more sensible to fence in the whole place straight away?

The band are preparing for their final session; a keyboard is exchanged for an accordion, tambourines and maracas are raised high, the singer adjusts his velvet bow tie, the guitarist drags a handkerchief across his face. The baby-faced band stick with popular dance tunes in spite of disco effects; blue smoke billowing up from the back of the stage and a tiresome sequence of flashing lights. The waiters are hurrying back and forward with last orders of beer and fried potatoes. The debris is being swept away, the potted hydrangeas plucked from the tables and set in serried ranks along the front of the stage like a little blue platoon.

At the far side of the floor you're standing, watching the dancers. It's a happy night, isn't it? Some of the students have been celebrating a bit too much – and why not – the queues for the toilets are spilling out into the main hall and, of course, when that happens the boys just step outside and relieve themselves in amongst the cars and courting couples, as the big, stunned moths whir around the spotlights.

We wouldn't have been found outside a dance hall, would we, pressed against a wall, not, at least, until the band had packed up their instruments, the lights had been turned off and the moths had fluttered back into the dark. When music was playing, we spent every moment on the floor. It was only later, at home, that it was difficult being close, only later that we slid apart; clumsy, tense, and the right words would never come to make those bad times better.

I'd curl up in a sheet, bury my face in the pillow, pretend to sleep because it was better than fighting. You would go out on the balcony and drink, or roam the streets all night.

You don't drink any more, I'm told. Or roam the streets. Your new girlfriend put her foot down. Dulcie; sweet by name and sweet by nature, I'm sure. Gets you in bed before daylight, I hear; she must be good for you. Pretty. Feminine. Petite. Goes to a good hairdresser too, I'd say. Must go out of town because she doesn't come to me. You've done well, finding such a girl to stay home for. She must be a calming influence. Pity she can't dance.

You're watching the dancers. Your attention is taken by this couple and that, those feet, hips, that clinch. I watch your eyes cast across the floor, slowly, studiously. When, finally, you look in my direction, I can return your gaze for only the briefest moment. Consider yourself kissed.

Norma E. Samúelsdóttir

From:
BRUISES IN THE COLOURS OF A RAINBOW

Translated from the Icelandic by Hulda V. Ritchie

CLEAR SKY

Two eyes met
softly
his
in mine

DIRTY GLASS

We looked
at the sky

the sunshine broke through
limpid water

unclean glass

countless
dirty
glasses

ROCKS

He jumped
over a pile of rocks
light as a feather

I clambered

THE TRUTH

Everybody knew the truth
I supported him
Everybody knew

Everybody knew the truth
and I
I knew the truth
that he was intelligent
his skin so soft

Clever
soft

Everybody knew

MARTYRDOM

Nice to hear your voice again, he said
come out to the wood
to the shack in the wood
and make love

Daily obligations
drudgery
merciless

walk
of martyrdom

mine...

BRUISES

hard bread
heavy fists

blows
hard blows

bruises

Desperate
flying
blows

His
Mine

and the orange colour

piercing
flame

WINTER NIGHT

I behind curtains
saw him walk
hand in her hand

Look
in
my
direction

STANDSTILL

Stare into the darkness
stood there and waited

snowflakes

northern lights

Stared up at the window

GIFTS

A little poem
in a language
that I understood

also bruises

gifts

that I looked upon

with pride

BOUND TO FAIL

The confirmation gift
a worn black book
with many proverbs

Unhappy are the lives
of those who take
responsibility
for others

Lesson for me

PROBABLY

Words ring
in my head

nobody hears them

If I were more often by myself
probably I would
understand
my words

THAW

The velvet snow
sunrays
melt the frozen drops

crystals
on the branches

two
white
beds

Iain Crichton Smith

AT THE STONES

She watched him as he bent down in the windy grass to study one of the stones. She felt cold but he didn't seem to be cold at all.

If you're looking for writing, she said, there won't be any.

I wasn't looking for writing, he said.

These stones, she thought, must be sunk deep in the ground. It was inconceivable how they had been transported.

It was Ronald's idea to visit this island to have a look at the Callanish stones. Of course the islanders had a Norse background and Ronald had studied Norse.

He had studied Norse, as well as Old English and Middle English which comprised his 'field'.

She looked wryly at the grass in front of her – her field.

As a matter of fact she rather liked the island, being used from her days in Wales to a rural community; indeed she remembered their days in Wales with untrammelled affection. If only they had remained there...

The brochure which told her about the stones shook in her hand.

They are not connected with the Druids according to this, she said.

No, they go back much further than that. Much much further than that.

In her mind she had a picture of robed Druids holding their hands up to the rising sun, though she couldn't think where she had come by it. The rising sun, the Druids, sacrifice.

Much further than that, he repeated, thousands of years. There were Druids in Colomba's time and that's only thirteen hundred years ago.

His round red-cheeked face glowed in the cold day. Often he looked quite cherubic.

It is all to do with the position of the stones, he said, and the moon rising at midsummer. At least I read that somewhere.

A boy and a girl with rucksacks were sitting in the hollow at the centre of the stones. They were eating sandwiches and drinking tea or coffee from a flask. She took shelter by the side of one of the tall bare stones.

They had remained five years in Wales when Ronald had

started his career. They were the happiest years of her life, she was sure. Neither the town nor the university was large and she knew a fair number of people and not only the ones connected with the university. And, of course, Ronald could speak Welsh after a fashion. She had tried to learn the language but failed.

There was a constellation of certain languages that Ronald knew, old Norse, Old and Middle English and old Welsh. And now he was having a look at Gaelic.

The names of villages ending in 'bost' are all Norse, he told her. There's Garrabost, Shawbost, Melbost, etc.

Sometimes she hated him; he was like a little doll, twinkling and well-meaning.

There is some theory about the shape of the hills over there, he said. Taken together they have the form of a recumbent woman. Can you see it?

At first she didn't and then she did.

That would be their goddess, he said. Imagine in mid-summer the moon rising there. They would have worshipped a goddess, an Earth Mother.

Then they had left Wales for Cambridge. Cambridge was a much more complicated place. She had found it cold, over-intellectual though Ronald avoided as many functions as he could; he had little small talk and wasn't witty.

The students too were different from the Welsh ones. They were more 'superior', more sophisticated, very bright.

The Welsh ones didn't stretch me so much, said Ronald. They didn't question much. And at seminars and tutorials they were less talkative.

And so he had to work much harder, wrote new lectures. Wales had made him lazy, he said.

The two young people sitting in the hollow looked like students, perhaps foreign ones, from Germany or France. She couldn't actually make out their language.

She had disliked Cambridge intensely, to put it mildly. There was a sort of formality and impersonality that threat-ened her. And Ronald didn't have time to talk to her. He was studying and writing harder than ever.

The calibre of student is much higher here, he said. And I have to keep up.

But I thought you knew your work already.

Yes, but you don't know what some of the students will unearth. They are more... unexpected.

And so he tried to insure against the unexpected.

And it was then that she began… expecting.

When she told him, he had taken it absent-mindedly as if it was nothing to do with him at all. It seemed he was so busy that he did not exist in the present. She herself had done some Anglo-Saxon when she had attended Aberdeen University; it was there that they had met.

She remembered certain poems about wanderers and sea-farers whose philosophy was to 'endure'. To endure loss and masters, unemployment. To endure storms, blizzards, turbulent seas.

He was taking photographs now.

How would he cope, she wondered, if something happened to her. He was buoyed up by her, his existence hung from hers, he was a little twinkling satellite of hers. He couldn't cook, or fix a plug. There were many quite simple things that he couldn't do. But all this was permissible in him because he was a professor. It was as if people equated brilliance with academe and forgave professors who couldn't change a lightbulb. How many Anglo-Saxon professors would it take to change a light-bulb? She smiled wryly.

The child was much more to her than it was to him. Now she had a reason to look after herself. Now she had a future. She felt happy, at times elated. For the life of her she couldn't imag-ine him as a father. And neither, she was sure, could he. She couldn't imagine him playing with a child, be it son or daughter. If the child spoke Middle English that might be different.

She looked at the configuration of the hills again. They did in fact look like a recumbent woman and she imagined a mild midsummer moon above them, a moon that would in autumn appear red.

The two young people stood up, put their rucksacks on, and walked towards the exit.

She had imagined the child in her womb as a tiny helmeted Anglo-Saxon. Her great trouble was that neither Ronald nor she had made any friends in Cambridge. She thought that Ron was boring, and she knew that in this environment she herself was boring. She was intimidated. But perhaps the child would not be boring, it might spring fully-armed from this hard bright Cambridge world. This world of quiet streets, bicycles, second-hand bookshops. Oh Cambridge so lovely in summer… but no place for a child.

Those big blank stones in front of her. Surely there should be writing on them. But then again they had been planted here before writing was invented. When people communicated in grunts perhaps as Ronald absent-mindedly did. Though he spoke more to her since his retirement. But he really was quite useless in the house, quite, quite useless ...

Quite, quite useless.

Could you come in here, please, he shouted to her from his study. The four walls were lined with books, and some were piled on the floor.

There's a book I want to get from the top shelf, he said, and told her the title. I haven't used it for a while but I believe it's there. I tried to stand on the step ladder but I felt dizzy.

He left her everything to do; he had surrendered the motions of his outward life to her. It was true that he sometimes felt dizzy, perhaps because of his intense study. Or perhaps he had only said that he felt dizzy. No, that was unfair; it would be wrong for an Anglo-Saxon scholar to tell a lie. On the other hand, he often evaded the 'shield wall'.

She should have tidied away the books on the floor, she should have been more careful where she had placed the ladders, he should have held the ladder more tightly... In her fall she knew immediately that the child had gone. As she tumbled on the books, as she lay recumbent among them, she knew that it was somehow fitting that she should find herself among books. In the blood. Later he looked at her, white-faced.

I'm sorry, he bumbled.

Sorry, sorry, sorry. She opened her eyes and then closed them. Her small helmeted Anglo-Saxon had gone. Yes, there was perhaps satisfaction to be discovered behind the sorrow. Who knew the intricacies of the human mind?

Now she saw him wearing his university gown and holding his knife up as he slit the child's throat while the red sun rose over the horizon. University gown, doctor's gown.

He walked to the car and waited helplessly for her to unlock the door. Her child, her only child, her twinkly-faced child, the one who endured to the end. The fresh-faced one who fussed about the stones on which nothing was written, whose origin was unintelligible, inconceivable, in the field, in the windy grassy field.

Morelle Smith

CHICKEN SAMOSAS AND THE HEART SUTRA

Silly girl, she is running round, she has lost her heart, she does not know where she has packed it, among all these bags and boxes piled in the rooms and hall, where could she have put it? Because it must be here, oh please God it must be here somewhere, I could not have, oh no I could not have left it behind, could I? Could I possibly, inadvertently, not meaning to, could I possibly have given it away before I left? So that no matter what box I look in, no matter how hard I search, it is not going to be there?

But how could I have done such a foolish thing, such a thoughtless thing. When might I have done that and how? And what connection does that have with my writing self, which also seems to be mislaid? I play with pieces of paper on my lovely Brazilian walnut desk, carved on two corners with a sun and moon. I sort through piles of papers that appear to have grown there, like mould. Once I came home to a beautiful and delicate arrangement on the kitchen table. I must have been away for some time. Perhaps it was in the summer. I do not remember the base, basis, or seed or jumping-off point for this delicate growth and even if I did I would not say, for it would sound pedestrian, prosaic, worse perhaps, it would conjure all kinds of associations you would not want to let near your imagination, hold it at arm's length.

So I will not refer to the basis of that growth but just comment on the delicacy of its fronds, the pale blue-green colour, its determination to grow, denying the fragility of what it has grown into. It brings both tenderness and respect, this fragile mould-construction. The touch of a finger evaporates it. I suppose I threw it away, though I might almost wish to have kept it, watched what it might do next. It could have been a companion in those days when I lost my heart and my writing self and needed company.

I played with pens and different coloured inks. I searched through jars of all varieties of writing implements – pens with soft tips, that snuggled into the page as if it was a blanket, or some long-lost companion, as if it was exactly what it needed, in that moment and forever; biros with caps and lacking caps – some that wrote, some that refused to write – some black, blue and red. Pencils – that would all need sharpening and that might all come in useful sometimes, though not right now, because I rarely write with pencil. And then there was my fountain pen, my favourite, with its smooth nib that travels across the page like a sea-journey with no waves, like a flight with no turbulence. I have another fountain pen, but its course is rougher, its journey makes a stronger impact on the page, it's not as quiet as my other one and besides, I do not know where it is, it's in one of these boxes piled in the back room, where many things are stacked away, just waiting to be found. Among them perhaps, my heart.

Is it possible – I hardly dare think of it, I leave that as a last resort though, but my mind keeps coming back to it, like the disaster you have tucked away in the mind's cellar, well out of reach of everyday life. Such things are the products of our darkest imaginations, worst fears, they do not exist, not really, a cellar after all, is hardly ever used, it's just there, waiting perhaps, no, it does not serve any useful purpose really, it's just there – and – no, I do not know why, it's always been there, that is all.

But – what if? Like leaving your wallet on the bus seat, like leaving the pram – with the baby in it, standing outside the shop – what if – that ultimate of disasters, that ultimate act of carelessness – has really happened?

If I left it behind, how could I have done that? When could it possibly have happened, what were the opportunities I had to give it away, let it go as carelessly as one might drop a bus ticket, when pulling something out of your purse? Had it happened that way, thoughtlessly, and by mistake, or had some unfamiliar part of me, going behind my back, as it were, made the gift deliberately and intentionally? If so, when could it have done that? I can recall no opportunities. When could I have handed over something as enormous as my heart? It is a wild and bulky object, not exactly cumbersome, but its boundaries are hard to define, it's difficult to pack it into any space, it always seems to spill over, no matter how large the container or how hard I try to compress it into something I've decided it ought to fit into.

If it does not want to go, it will not budge, like some irrational cat that will not get into its box, even though it's time to catch the train. It does not listen to reason or train schedules, it just sits there and gets vicious and defensive if you try to force it. I cannot imagine my heart going willingly away from me, no matter in how roomy or comfortable a container.

I search back in my mind, trying to remember what might have passed between us, from me to him. I remember the samosas I took round for us to eat, the day he left. But they hardly seemed adequate to contain my heart. Two chicken samosas. Delicious they were. He had bought samosas too. Vegetable ones. I heated them up in the oven. And we had one vegetable one and one chicken one each.

I heated them in the oven. Now why did I do that, when it was his place and only the second time I had been there? The first time, I had arrived in the afternoon. I had walked across town in the rain to where he lived. To see him? You walked miles in the rain, to see him? Yes. Well no, not exactly, not the way you make it sound. I wanted to walk anyway, I had been sitting in some cafe, me and my writing self, perhaps me and my heart as well, I am fairly certain that my heart was there as well, because I felt good, in this writing cafe, with the rain outside. And after that, wanted to walk, I like walking in the city, especially after sitting in a cafe, drinking coffee, yes, especially then. And the rain, I don't mind the rain, I mean it was not pouring down, I do not think it was as heavy as that, the sky was grizzly grey and the rain was fairly steady and of course I did not have an umbrella because it had not been raining that morning when I left.

I thought I was going to be working on the computer that day, took the bus to Rosa's, but there was no answer when I rang the bell. Waited, and rang again. And though I have a key and normally I would have let myself in, I had forgotten it, that day. And so, standing outside the door, I felt quite good that I would not be working, a small plan was forming in my mind already so I turned round and walked back into the city, did not even catch a bus, even then you see, I wanted to walk.

And after I had sat in the cafe with my writing self and heart, I wanted to walk some more and so, even though the rain had started, that's what I did. A little bit of rain has never put me off if my heart is in it. And my heart, at that point, definitely was. My mind played with the idea, tossing it backwards and forwards – should I go? I asked my mind. Why not? my mind replied. He did say he would like it if you called in anytime and even though you said you would be working today – as you thought you would – and so he will not be expecting you, I'm sure it will be alright – I knew it would be alright. Some part of me knew. Perhaps it was my heart. Perhaps it was my writing self, all high and careless and tripping up with words, all joyous in the rain. It did not appear to care, one way or the other, but often it knows more than any other part of me, because it stretches high and has a good view over time and space and smiles to itself, a joyous smile, it does not present factual packages, it just knows as the Buddha knows and rejoices in the knowing.

My heart must have been in there as well, as she always loves the company of my writing self and – I would almost say – never seems happier than when she is with him. And then of course, there were my feet, my trusty guides. At times when I am not sure what to do, when my mind – which has a dual nature, just like any other mind I'm sure and is happy to carry on a cheerful conversation with itself – but at times when there is no agreement, when one part suggests one thing, leans to one side and the other backs up or represents some alternative, it's my feet I turn to.

OK feet I say, I'm not sure what to do here, not sure what way to go, what direction to go in, what course to follow. My mind has foundered in duality, it is divided and does not know which way to turn. I cannot stand indefinitely on this street corner, so it's up to you. And I let my feet take me in the direction that they choose. My feet get me out of duality, my feet see me through.

That afternoon, there really was no conflict. My writing self was there, my heart, my mind could not resist a quick debate, because it takes that chance at the slightest opportunity, it likes so much to talk to itself, if there is no-one else to talk to – but it soon reaches agreement and my feet had no doubt in them, they were happy to keep going.

The rain dripped steadily but not torrentially and there was no buffeting wind to block my path, as there often is, in this city. By the time I arrived though my hair was dripping with rain. Not that it bothered me, but I must have looked as though I had made some long and difficult journey, just to see him. He got me a towel for my hair, put on the kettle and kept saying how good it was to see me.

And so we sat there, drinking first coffee and then tea, swapping stories I suppose, I cannot remember anything we talked about, but we must have talked of something for we sat there for two hours and I am sure we did not just sit staring at each other, I would have remembered that. I brought nothing with me then, except myself and a good portion of the rain.

Between that time and my second and last visit, before he left, we did all kinds of things. But I did not give him anything. Except for some over-spicy curry, I remember now, and some slightly burnt dahl, that was the evening we went round to see a friend of his. But the meal was cooked already, it was not made with him in mind, it had to be reheated and besides, it really was not very good, although he said that he enjoyed it.

But on the second visit, there were those samosas, tasting like no samosas have ever tasted before, bought fresh from Mrs Unis's on Dalry Road, made on the premises. It reminded me of India. So much. And in his flat, I heated them in the oven, triangular shaped objects, no bigger, I would say, than the size of someone's heart. But not of mine, because mine refuses to be measured, refuses to conform to any size at all. And I remember now, I heated them and made the tea because he was organising things, he was packing up, he had lots of things to do and I was only there – to see him off I suppose, to keep him company while he got his things together. So it made sense that I should do that, while he looked through files, pulled clothes out of drawers, put things leisurely in boxes and trunks, talked on the telephone.

He's not the kind of person who rushes about and gets himself all wound up, who gets his thoughts in knots and then despairs of the tangles in his mind. Methodical mind, slowly pursuing order, with no hurry and no angst, just moving, in a nomadic, wandering fashion, leisurely, unhurried, to his goal. While my mind jumps like a gnat, turns somersaults, my acrobatic mind, swinging on trapezes and scaring itself when it looks down, juggling delightedly with its contents, ideas turning in circles, being caught, being thrown up in the air – oh, my mind delights in these kinds of aeronautics, it has a pilot's ambitions, twirling and skimming high above the ground.

So while he moved slowly, with increasing certainty and order, from room to room, I bounced and jiggled on the sofa, reading Rimbaud, reading Burns, reading about England's sacred sites, playing tapes, playing Dire Straits, playing Aly Bain, playing Sibelius, wriggling on the sofa. Jumping up and down, making cups of tea.

Then, when he sat down, I remember – and now I think I

have it. I think I have that moment when I handed him my heart. Of course. How could I have forgotten that?

It was something I had written, written with him in mind, written – for him. I do not write to order, have never done such a thing, but this was – ordered in a way, some part of me made the request, in my mind's restaurant, where all kinds of dishes are served on request, if my mind is in its happy, experimental mood, it searches among its recipes, it's happy to oblige. Or it was that time. It hummed to itself as it went about, collecting ingredients.

Afterwards, I thought it was not such a good poem, but it had two lines in it I liked and they were:

> The night turns its black page,
> Folds the memory of light.

And because of them I thought – this is good, this is good enough to give to him, yes, this is alright, it will do. I looked for things to put in this poem, this collage I wanted to make for him. It was like making a sculpture, one of these things I hang on the wall, made from sticks and wool, shells, feathers, grasses, leaves, dried berries.

Making this poem was like that and I did not know that making poems was like arranging flowers, but this one was, a little bit, only those two lines came out of nowhere, they were not part of the recipe, they were the magic created from the combination, they were the path down to the secret garden, they were the forbidden fruit, forbidden because the taste of ecstasy on unaccustomed lips could bring about a grieving from the lonely human people, all garden-gone and birdsong empty, the lonely human rag-pickers, all mourning, all heimweh, no, this fruit is too much reminding and that we cannot bear. 'Too much reality –' that is food too sensitive for us. Or it was. Now, it is not. Now, that garden is accessible to strong climbers and swimmers with powerful lungs, it is possible, look, we are breathing, we are coming up for air, through the underwater tunnel, a north-west passage that we did not know existed. We are breathing, and we fill our lungs with air, look, we have arrived, we have come home.

With this piece of arrival in the poem, with this sunken garden that you come across, unexpected at sundown, it was alright, I thought that it would do. I took the first two lines from something I had written just the day before, from the feeling that I had, the taste of how it felt, one evening on my own. It tasted calm, tasted peaceful, tasted subtle, strawberries mixed in with cream taste, crushed summer underneath the tongue. I looked at the sentence and I saw it was two lines, that's what it was, only I did not know that when I wrote it. So I put them in at the beginning. Buddha-lines. Saying what they are not. Which is a good device to leave space for what is. Which cannot be put into words. Buddha-lines, they are a bit like housework, it is not the work you see, it is the absence of confusion and disorder, the absence of disarray. And the absence makes what is there, shine. It is subtle, this Buddha-order, you need to sharpen your perceptions to see much of it at all. But get used to it and you want nothing else but this, this polished quality to life, this breathing of objects that are loved and cared for and that know it.

So the Buddha-lines, what they do is to clear the grime, the dust, the twigs and gritty stones we carry in from outside, inadvertently, all the muddy memories, the little anger antics and the irritation rashes, the little mourning drops, the rustling sadnesses, all the fallen vegetables from the market stalls we bring in with us from the street. These are swept and dusted, cleaned off and dried out, because we care about our mind, our temple, our home, our sanctuary. And it's not so much the absence of detritus, or emotional left-overs, it's the caring that shines them. When everything extraneous is washed off, brushed away, what is revealed is love.

So I began –

> This is not a gap, a pain,
> It is no kind of grief at all.

I cleaned up my memory of that walk we took by the river, up to the Art Gallery, with the sun going down. I cleaned it and polished it and found the moment when everything was still, when it all came together. For often there is a moment, a stillness and on either side of that, there is before and there is an after, but in special memories there often is a moment, no matter how short or long that moment is, you cannot define it by a measurement of time, you recognise it by its quality of being and there is a stillness there, a timelessness and when you bring it back into your memory you can relive it, yes, you can feel it.

So I walked back into that moment, over and over again, I

walked back in and arrived at the core of it, its centre, its rhythmic, timeless heart. Its place of stillness and expansion, its place of wide, wide wings. And over and over, I walked back in and we were standing there, at the top of the steps leading up from the river, looking back at the sun, caught in its net of clouds, sun low in the sky, sun on a level with us, shining straight into our faces. And how we stood there and the light was deep orange/yellow on our hands and faces and our faces glowed in that deep light. This is the moment when we felt the breath of some enfolding, some enormous wings. And stood still, not wanting, ever, to forget the feel of them.

And when all that it is not, is brushed away, all that this moment is not, is lifted from it, what is revealed is love.

And so you see, although I did not know it then, it was my heart who wandered into the restaurant of my mind, sat down, in an unobtrusive way, at a table in a dimly-lit recess and waited for my mind to notice it and then made its request. My mind could not object to this quiet-spoken customer. The people it disliked were the ones who talked too loudly, the ones who made demands. My mind is manager, head chef and waiter, all rolled into one and if he decides he does not want to do what's asked of him, he simply will not do it. He has absolute – or as he thinks – control and he rather likes to flaunt that sometimes, he likes to show demanding, overbearing customers that he is boss, there will be no rebellion here, no coups du restaurant, he can just refuse, he can say no and if he feels like it, he will.

But my heart with its request, he found a pleasing customer and so he puffed up all his feathers and put himself out to please.

And this is what he came up with. And though he would be the first to admit that those two lines are the magic and the making of it and they were not exactly chosen by him, they appeared, like feathers fallen from those great wings, gifts they were, still, he knows really, that the best is not chosen by him so much as being a result of the mixture, the combination that he has chosen, so, at his best, he is a conduit for angel feathers, he is a vessel and a messenger from other realms, just as he is not really the boss of the restaurant, not the ultimate authority or source of all this fare, but he is still the most visible producer and anyone who wants to get close to the one who has really set it up, has to go through him, so they have to treat him well.

My heart, my mind, my writing self, they all combined to

make this and I handed it to him before he left. And I did not even know what I was doing. I handed it to him and now I am sure, when I look back at it, that was the moment when I handed him my heart. For this is something I just do not do. If I write things from a garden that a person has evoked in me, I do not even let them read it, never mind give it to them. But with him, I had no fear, with him I felt it was alright, I handed it to him and he read it and there was this softness in his voice when he said he really liked it, a softness in his voice when he said he would read it every day. For he was leaving, he was travelling, he was going far away and he said 'I'll read it every day'.

Now he has this part of me with him and that is why I cannot find it in my house. His hands are holding what I gave him, it is no longer in my hands and there is nothing, nothing I can do to change that. I cannot take it back, it is too late for that. It is done and that is why I've given up on searching through the boxes in my house, for something that I know now, is not there. A part of me has gone travelling with him, I can only wait till he comes back, to be with it again.

So that what is required now of me, is acceptance. Trust. And more Buddha-words from the Heart Sutra.

'Gone, gone, all gone, safely passed to the other shore.' And with that clearing off of all that is extraneous, what is revealed is love.

And so when he phones to say he is back in Europe, will I join him TOOT SWEET I know it is not just him I am meeting up with, it is myself as well, my best self, my heart self and I say 'yes', there is no question here, 'yes' I say, 'Oh yes'.

Lisa Snell

FEARTIE

Hid wis th Saiturday nicht o Shoppin Week, weel th early evenin, wi th grimlins comin doon. Jest efter th Stromness against Kirkwall match. Wi wur in a fine guid mood, Stromness hid won an abody hid gaan tae th ale hoose fur twa drams tae celebrate efterwards. Us young eens hid been gaen twa pound fur chips ur candy floss, tae keep us quiet an oot o the road so th owlder eens could hae some peace. Wi aal gied peltin up th street, fair chuffed tae hae some free time afore th nightly chorus o scraikin mithers stairted aboot baithtime.

Thir wis a wee group o us thit hung aboot tagaither, an wur furiver gettin intae trouble o some kin or anither. Thur wus me, Peedie Stevenson hoo wis that hefty he coodnae be peedie if he tried, Sproot who wis me own age an hid sticky-up reed hair thit widnae stay doon, Trev who wis th bairn cos he wis only six, an Big Malkie who wis wur kindae leader cos he wis th owldist an th strongest it nearly bein therteen. Ah'm Chimmy an ah'm ten year owld. Ma mither caals me Chames, bit aal ma pals caa me Chimmy.

Onyway, wi wur aal ootside o th chippy wi wur steemin peedie pokes o paper whin th auld witchy wifey cam oot o th close across th street. She's an aald crone waar disnae spik tae onybody cept th folk in her heid. She's gey queer lik, an stinks too. Ma mither sais hid's cos she drinks Mither's Ruin, bit th auld wife disnae hae ony bairns so I dinnae think she kin be richt. Whin she came oot o th close she stoppit an luikit it us. She glecked it us fur twa meenits, thin gaed harein up th street is though her erse wis on fire. Weel, wi jest kindae watched her gaan doon th street, no richt sure whit way she wis so feart o a group o bairns. Thin Malkie hid his bright idea.

'C'mon lads, lit's follow the witchy wife an see if wi kin caitch her on her broomstick!'

He wis backit up by Peedie, waar said he wisnae feart o onythin cos nuthin wis bigger thin he wis. Wi didnae really believe aal th stories wi got telt aboot the auld wife, an the Bairn wis fair excited aboot mebee seein a proper witch on a broomstick, so wi aal pelted up th street tae catch up wi her.

As wi gied roond th corner at th end o th street wi saa her walkin tae her hoose up th close. Wi slowed doon, an Malkie telt is tae copy whit he did. He ran across th street, an flattened himsel against th waal lik aal th proper detectiffs do. Wi aal copied, thin he peepit roond th corner. Wi aal did th saim, an wir jest in time tae see the auld wife gaan intae her hoose an shuttin th door.

'Richt,' whispered Malkie, 'Wur gaan tae see if wi kin git intae hir hoose.'

Ah felt Sproot move a wee bit. 'Ur ye mad,' he hissed, 'or wur ye jest born stupeed? Ye'll no manage tae git intae th hoose. Naebody's managed hid afore.'

Th rest o us held wur breath. Folk didnae live fur long if they caaled Big Malkie stupeed. Malkie turned roond an luikit it Sproot.

'Ur ye sayin me big brother's a liar? Him an twa o his pals gied intae hir hoose wioot bein seen, an they got oot alive. Ye're jest a big muckle feartie.'

Aal o us turned an luikit it Sproot. His face wis fair reed, lik his hair. Th waan way tae mak Sproot mad is tae caal him a feartie, but he didnae dare dae onythin cos Malkie wis that big, an he hid owlder brithers thit wir aboot six feet taal. Ah pattit his showlder so he kent ah didnae much care fur Big Malkie either.

Whin wi turned roond again Malkie wis gone. Thin wi herd a hiss fae up th close. In th lich to th grimlins wi cuild jest mak oot th shaip o Malkie it th lane it th side o th witchy wife's hoose.

'C'mere afore onybody sees ye!'

Tryin tae be as quiet aan cool is Chames Bond, wi aal ran up tae wur Malkie wis standin. Th Bairn wis that excited he wis near peein himsel.

'Whit dae wi dae noo?'

This wis fae Peedie, waar wanted tae be is cool is Malkie an his owlder brithers.

'The ownly way tae git in is throo th brocken skylight in th ruif. Wi hif tae clim up th waa it th back an git ontae th ruif that way.'

Wi wur aal listenin carefully, watchin Malkie's face is he spok. He luikit it the Bairn, who wis tryin no tae pee himsel.

'Ah dinna think hid's a guid idea tae hae th Bairn wi us. He'll mebbe git is intae trouble.'

Th Bairn luikit up wi his eyes aal shiny lik he wis gaan tae greet. He crossed his legs even hairder, thin stairted tae jump up an doon. Thir wis a big owld floower pot next tae the waan waal, wi a big deid floower in hid. I tuik th Bairn ower tae hid an telt him tae pee in there. Whin he wis daein that, I luiket it Malkie.

'Wi cannae mak th Bairn go haim noo. He'll clipe on us thin wur faithers'll tan wur hides th morn. Kin we no jest lit him tag along? He'll likly no be ony bother, he's only peedie.'

Malkie thowt aboot hid fur a meenit, thin 'Aalright, ah suppose so. Bit ye're tae luik efter him. If onythin happens tae him hid's ye'r fault.'

The Bairn appeared aside me, an took haad o me hand. Ah shuik hid aff, thin glowered it Malkie's back is he led is doon tae th back waal. Th waal wis richt next tae a windae in th witchy wife's hoose, so wi hid tae be quick an careful no tae be seen. Wance up on th waal wi hid tae git up on th ruif o th hoose. Malkie gied up first, thin Sproot. I handed up th Bairn tae Sproot, thin climmered up mesel. Thin, wi a bit o help fae us, Peedie dragged hissel up tae. Thir wis a noise fae th hoose nixt door. A man appeared it th windae, aan luikit oot. 'Bluidy aald cats.' Wi herd th windae shut, an brethed oot.

'We'll hae tae be careful wi dinna git caught, so dinna mak ony racket fur goodness sake,' hissed Malkie. He climmered up th ruif tae th brocken skylight aan we waatched is he opened hid wi his pocket knife.

'C'mon you lot, quick!'

Wi aal scrambled up th ruif aan gaithered roond th hole.

'Waar's gaan first? Ah dinna think ah'll mainage tae git in throo such a peedie hole,' asked Peedie.

'Wi need some een thit's light an willna mak a racket an is allso smaal enough tae fit in throo th hole.'

Me an Sproot luikit it each ither. Hid couldnae be th Bairn, he wis too smaal tae be put throo th hole first, aan he'd likly clatter win he hit th flair. Hid wid hiff tae be waan o us pair.

Sproot spoke.

'Ah think hid shuid be Chimmy. Ah'd likly clatter whin ah hit th flair.'

Malkie luikit it me, thin so did abody else. Ah stairted tae shak me heid, 'Not a chance, ye'll no git me gaan first doon th hole.'

'Bit c'mon Chimmy. Ye always said ye wanted tae be lik Chames Bond did ye no? Here's yer chance. Aa th lassies lik a hero.'

Ah thowt aboot hid fur a meenit. Ah'd aye wanted tae be lik Chames Bond, but ah didnae want tae be a hero if hid meant ah had tae git a kiss aaf th lassies. Yin wir horrible, an th lassies aye ran aff gigglin an laffin an left me wi a reed face. Ah luikit it Malkie.

'Dae ah have tae git a kiss?'

Malkie laffed. 'No unless ye want tae. Ye'll no be made tae git a kiss if ye dinnae want tae.'

Ah thowt aboot hid again fur a meenit.

'Aalright thin, ah'll go in first.'

Th first thing ah saw doon th hole wis aal this weird shaips an lumps lyin aboot on th flair o th attic. Hid wis a fair drop doon tae th flair, bit ah wis mair feart o me airms bein pulled oot o th sockets thin makin a rummle whin ah fell. Malkie hid waan o me airms an Peedie hid a haud o th ither, an they wir tryin tae lower me doon slow lik. Whin ah wis aboot a foot aaf th flair ah heard a yelp thin ah fell wi a great muckle rummle intae a heap. Throo aal th cloods o stoor ah heard Malkie whisperin'.

'Ur ye aal richt Chimmy? Ye're no deid ur ye? Peedie lit go o yer airm cos th eejit wis tryin tae tak a sweetie oot o is pooch. Ye made a fair rummle. P'raps wi should've put doon Sproot first.'

Th stoor wis makin me eyes waater, an ah wis howkin cos hid wis aal dry in me throat. Hid wis stairtin tae settle noo, an ah cuid see things mair clearly. This big thin shaip stairted tae faal towards me an ah jumpit back quick lik. Hid kindae fell ower by me feet. Ah got a fair shock, ah'm tellin ye. Hid wis yin o thae auld brushes fur sweepin th flair, ken, a broomstick. Mebbe Malkie wis richt efter aal.

'Chimmy!'

Ah luiked up an saw Sproot's tackety boots danglin in front o me face.

'Grab a haud o im will ye afore ah lit go. An fur God's sake dinna mak a noise!'

Ah did as ah wis telt, an soon Sproot wis aside me rubbin his airmpits.

'Yon Malkie's a bugger an no mistake,' he whispered, 'he near hid me airms oot o th sockets!'

Nixt doon wis th Bairn, waar gied aaf tae explore. Whin wi luiked roond wi saw th Bairn pickin up th broomstick aaf th flair waar hid'd faaen. Malkie's een gied as roond is saucers an he made a low whiskin soond.

'Weel lads, whit did ah tell ye? Sure as ah'm standin here th witch wife's a proper witch, an there's aal th proof ye need.'

Wi aal gazed it th broom, an th Bairn lat it draap tae th flair again is if he'd been bitten. In th gloom o th peedie room wi aal th strange shaips an th scufflins o the mice, th Bairn wisnae feelin so brave noo, an grabbit a haud o me breeks, fair feart bi whit Malkie hid jist said. In th peedie gren o licht wi cuid see aal sorts o junk lyin aroon, a'thing fae brocken chairs an auld bits o cairpit tae cairdboard boxes an big lither trunks aal tied wi string. Whilst is fower stuid in a peedie group tryin no tae lit on wi wur fair spookit, Malkie wis ower in waan corner near a lumpy owld sofa, tryin tae open th door. Thir wis a big crack, an a yellowy licht appeared in th corner, showin up Malkie's face wi hid's eerie glow. Yon colour didnae improve im any. He beckoned tae is.

'Git ower here an dinna mak a racket!'

Wi scurried ower, trippin ower boxes an ither junk. Peedie tripped up it waan side an fell heavy lik against a low rafter. Nixt thin wi kent thir wis a half a dizzen bats flyin oot past wir heids. This wis too muckle fur th Bairn waar screeched lik a wild thing.

Sproot grabbit is heid an clampt is hand ower th Bairn's mooth. Malkie cam bowlderin ower fae th door an grabbit me airm.

'Whit dae ye think ye're playin it min? If ye dinna shtoop we'll no git oot o here alive!'

He pickit up th Bairn an gaed im a piggy back, thin turned roond an glared it is.

'Dae ye think ye'll manage tae luik efter yersells an no git is caught? Ah'm stairtin tae wish ah'd no tane ye aal wi me, ye're too peedie tae be able tae dae this profeshonally lik Chames Bond.'

Whin Malkie gaed th wurd he opened th door an wi all held wur breth whin hid creakit. Whit wid she dae tae is if we git caught? Surely she widnae mak is intae peedie puddocks lik they did in th stories? Th ownly way tae mak is back tae normal is tae git a kiss aaf a lassie. Ah didnae care much fur that lark.

Malkie stairted doon the stair an wi aal followed. Thir wis only aboot a half a dizzen steps doon, bit they creakit an worked such a waark thit wi thowt we'd be turned intae peedie puddocks fur sure. Even Malkie wis fair feart o whit wid happen if wi got caught. Me mither wid skin me alive if ah wis lit fur me baith.

Wi herd a scuffle doon below is. Wi aal tensed up an held wir breth. Me hert wis gaan ten tae th dizzen, me legs wur aal wobbly an ah felt seeck. O me giddy aunt, whit if wi didnae git oot o here alive?

A shaip appeared it th buddum o th stairs, thin stairted tae come up thim. Malkie hid opened th door nearest tae im an found a cupboard. He stairted tae bundle abody intae it afore she came, thin grabbit me airm an pullit me in tae. Ah wis feelin worse thin afore. Ah felt hot, me mooth wis dry an me legs wur aal shaky. Ah've niver faintit afore, bit thin everythin gied black...

Whin ah cam roond ah wis in Malkie's airms, an Sproot hid a haud o me feet. Ah tried tae git thim tae pit me doon bit they widnae. Nixt thin ah ken, wur bowlderin doon the stair, an ah'm bumpin up an doon worse thin gittin a dose o th bumps. Wance wi wur doon th stair they still didnae lit me go, bit kept on runnin along th lobby an oot o th door. Wance wi wur doon th close they pit me doon, an me legs gave way fae under me.

'Whit happent ye, min?' peched Peedie, 'Waan meenit ye're fine, th nixt ye're oot fur the coont an me an Sproot hid tae cairy ye oot afore th witchy wife cam oot o her room an caught is.'

Ah felt ma face go reed, thin Malkie joined in.

'Aye, fine Chames Bond ye'd mak if ye collapse in a deid faint every time ye're unner pressure! Nae fear o haein tae kiss th lassies if ye cannae stay awake long enough!'

Abody wis laffin, an th Bairn wis pettin sum auld moggy, whin wi herd someen shoutin. Wi aal listened, thin herd hid again.

'Peedie boys, Ah hae sweeties fur peedie boys.'

Wi all jumpit up and turned roond. Th witchy wife wis it th door o her hoose, beckonin tae is. Ah felt ma knees go aal weak again. She kept beckonin tae is.

'Ah think she waants ane o is tae git th sweeties aff her.' Malkie spoke. Sproot luikit it me.

'Ah think Chimmy shuid dae is Chames Bond bit again.'

Ah glared it im, bit too late. 'Aye, ah think so tae,' This wis fae Peedie.

'Weel ye'll be sorry whin she zaps me wi her powers an kills me.'

Ah gied slowly up th close, no luikin till th last meenit. She wis aaful peedie an wizened, no relly lik a witch it aal. Hir gums wir aal worn so's aal ye cuid see wir her gums wi peedie white bits in thim. Ah stoppit in front o her aan luikit doon. She held oot th poke.

'Sweeties fur peedie boys. Peedie boys lik sweeties.'

She placed thim in me hand. They wir pear drops. Magic! Ah luikit hir in th face.

'Thanks missus.'

Ah ran back doon th close tae share thim oot. Malkie grinnt it me an pattit me on th back.

'Ye're no sich a bad Chames Bond efter aal. Ye'd better waatch oot fur th lassies!'

Ah grinnt it im, sookin a pear drop. Thin ah heard th soond o me mither screckin. Oh naa, ah'm late fur me baith.

'See ye th morn?'

Malkie grinnt. 'Aye, be seein ye th morn.'

Baithtime wudna be so bad efter aal.

Yvonne Spence

A FEW LUXURIES

The birds have long since gone. No snow has fallen yet, but its
bitter foretaste is in the air. Over an hour ago I went out to the
stack for peats, and the wind tore through my thick winter coat
as though it was a flimsy cotton dress. I'm still cold. It's freezing here. Bloody freezing.

He hates it when I swear, says it's a bad example in front
of the girls. Wants them to grow up right in the head, not like
him – heard too much swearing as a bairn, he says. He's right,
I know it, but the girls are at school. There are times, when
I'm on my own like this, that I stop working and just scream
obscenities. Nobody can hear; the nearest house is quarter of a
mile away. It eases the pressure.

I've thought about leaving. God knows, I've thought
about it often enough.

'I couldna live withoot de, Laura,' he says.

So I stay.

I know what they say round here. Through the shop window I've seen the mouths wagging, and I've seen the suspended
lips when I walk through the door. By the time I've picked up a
basket, thrown in a *Shetland Times*, and headed for the frozen
vegetables they recover their wits.

'You're looking well Laura.' That would be Winnie.

'How are da bairns? Is Marianne enjoying da school?'
Nessie.

'She's never dat age already is she?' Winnie again.

'It seems no time since you came here, a slip of a lass, and
Callum saying he'd have to settle down noo he wis married.'
That was the dig. Carefully chosen words intended to pierce
me. For I was the outsider who stole Callum from Nessie's
daughter. Of course marriage didn't settle Callum down; we all
knew that. And we all knew the husband Hazel eventually got
was a much better catch than mine.

'My Hazel's boy started at da school dis year too. In
Jeddah.' A flick of the head to emphasise the importance of
Jeddah, before she landed the final stinger. 'Mick's company
pays for him tae go tae an English speaking one.'

I leaned into the freezer and picked up some peas and
sweetcorn. I noticed a black forest gateau in Nessie's basket,

and my mouth watered. There was another one in the freezer.

'Hazel and da bairns are coming hame for Christmas. You'll hae tae come along and see them.' I couldn't say if she was talking to Winnie or me.

Winnie answered. 'She's done well for herself, your Hazel.'

I put the cake back and squeezed past them; balloons of women, squashed into Crimplene frocks, their faces bursting out from nylon parka hoods, and thick nylons wrinkling around swollen ankles. I threw a wholemeal loaf into my basket.

Nessie whispered loudly to Winnie. 'Aye, it's a good job she never married Callum, dat one is welcome tae him.'

I was meant to hear it, but not admit I'd heard, and I played my part as always instead of telling her how he built the kids a playhouse in the yard, how he put up a swing, taught them to swim and tells them bedtime stories, and how they adore him. All she knows is the drinking, she doesn't want to know anything else.

I used to work in a bank, but it's too far into Lerwick every day when you have kids; so when I fell pregnant I did a machine knitting course at the FE College. Every since I've made jumpers. Day after bloody day I blend rows of beige, brown and white into 'natural' Fair Isles. He lost the first job when I was five months pregnant so I began knitting three days after Colleen was born. His next job lasted six months, and after that he was on a fishing boat. Silly fool that I was I thought we would do fine then, but when they couldn't put out to sea because of bad weather the money he'd made went down his throat.

'It's a miserable job Laura, I need some escape when I get hame,' he would say.

'And whit aboot me? Whit aboot the bairns? Whit sort of escape do we hae?'

'You can't imagine da hell it is oot dere, Laura.'

'I ken the hell it is here.'

That's how it stayed till he'd had enough of being wet and stinking, and I'd had enough of him boozing away money that should have fed the kids.

I suppose it was pride that made me stay. I couldn't bear to let my mother know she had been right. I couldn't bear to imagine the muttering from Nessie and Winnie as I left. And not just them. I used to go to the dancing; in the toilets I'd overhear the women re-touching their make-up and gossip.

Click, the lipstick snaps open, and the mouth with it. 'Has du seen da state of Callum again?'

Hairspray fizzes before someone replies. 'God, he asked me tae do da Boston Two Step. He could hardly stand let alone dance, and his shirt was covered in sick.' I recognise this laughing voice; Sheila, niece of Nessie, cousin of Hazel.

'Imagine dat coming tae bed wi you – yeuch. Damn, dis mascara has smudged.'

'Here take dis tissue. God kens why she puts up wi him; I'd hae kicked him out long ago.'

'Well, dey say she's a terrible nag, so you canna really blame him. She drives him tae it.' Handbags click closed, the door creaks and they have gone. In the silence they leave behind I wonder – did I drive him to it? I wait a while before I come out, long enough to avoid bumping into them outside.

I seem to live my life in shadows, hearing other people's lives going on around me. It gets that way when you are ashamed of your own life; it's hard to go out at all. So I daydream instead. Though this knitting can get boring, it gives me plenty of time to dream. I watch the birds flying south and think about the designer garments I make doing the same. Everything I knit is exported, every garment labelled *Designed and hand framed in the Shetland Isles*. I imagine well-heeled women in Japan, Italy, Singapore and Los Angeles strutting about in their Fair Isles. I doubt if they ever wonder about the person who made their fancy clothes, and God alone knows what they want with woolly jumpers living in places like that. We went to Majorca on our honeymoon, and the last thing I'd have wanted was a woolly jumper

I'm thinking about this when I notice the snow. The first flakes of the year, swirling in the darkening air, blown by the gale onto the window. There's a myth that since we're surrounded by water it never gets cold here like it does down south. Sure, without the Gulf Stream we'd be six feet in snow from November to March like in Newfoundland or Norway. But the wind. It can sniff out the tiniest crack in a window, the minutest gap under a door. I've got draught excluders at every door and a fire burning the devil would be proud of, yet still the wind manages to find me. Sometimes I think the chill is inside me, coming from my heart.

He's due home today. He works in the oil now, on a survey

boat; he's finally using his degree. He rang me from Aberdeen last night, after his boat docked.

'I'll never make it, Laura. I canna manage through Christmas,' he said.

'Du's managed nearly a year,' I said. 'Du'll be fine.'

'Du kens whit last year was like. I canna do it, Laura.'

'We can stay at hame, just da four of us. Nae visitors, nae visiting.'

'Dey always come. It's expected. Can du imagine my faither when I say I'm no haeing a Christmas dram? He'll go crazy. And I can guess whit folk'll say if I stay at hame all Christmas and New Year. I canna do it, Laura.' The pips went.

Callum's right. Every year his folk come over, and his dad is usually well oiled before they even get here, been out around the neighbours. He staggers in with his half-bottle, and the pair of them sit down for a Christmas dram. I try to finish making the dinner while his mum nips my head about the size of the turkey (too big, though that doesn't stop her wanting seconds), the size of the tree and the quantity of decorations the girls and I have put up (a total waste of money).

'Is anybody watching dis rubbish?' she says year after year, switching the TV off. 'Dat's better, da noise aboot sends me crazy.'

It's a silly habit I suppose, but since I was a teenager I've liked to watch the Christmas Top Of The Pops. I really prefer Country and Western or a bit of Soul music to all this Rap and House nowadays, but I like to keep my own little tradition. Still, I bite the urge to remind her whose house it is.

'Why don't you take Granny into da sitting room and show her your presents?' I ask the girls, even though it always elicits the same response from Granny.

'Bairns these days get far too many presents; I was happy wi a doll and an apple and orange frae Santa. Dere's no enough hours in da day tae play wi all dis trash.' But they are already dragging her from the kitchen. I switch the TV back on.

The arguments start while we're eating. Callum's dad wants to know when he's going to stop arsing about and put all those years of college they paid for to some use.

'You paid for, dat's a good ane,' Callum replies. 'I never saw a penny frae you.'

Then his mum wants to know when he's going to come over and fix their car, Hoover, transistor, and could somebody please switch that racket off, she can't hear herself think. Colleen learned fast; she's been switching the TV off since she was three.

'Dat's better.' Granny heaves a big sigh, and gulps her alcohol-free wine.

'Could we no hae a proper drink instead o' dis rabbit piss.'

The girls giggle, then sensing the atmosphere, study their food.

'Granddad!' Granny slams her glass down.

'Ach shut de moaning, du auld fool.'

'It's Christmas. Can du not be civil just one day of the year?'

'Does anybody need more turkey?' I ask, my voice shrivelling in the heat of their rage.

'Stuff da turkey!' Granddad yells, and he roars with laughter.

It gets worse every year.

While the men sleep it off Granny watches the Queen, I do the dishes, and the first carload of drunks tumbles into our yard.

'Yoho lass, Merry Christmas,' they bellow.

'Come in by and hae a dram,' Callum shouts, and they tramp through my kitchen in mucky boots, brandishing half-bottles of whisky.

The girls come running, 'Yon men smell, and dey're blowing fags.'

'Why don't you sit at da table and do your new jigsaw?'

Granny appears. 'Da Sound of Music is on. I think I'll watch it in here.'

There have been times when the boozing has gone on till daylight, which mid-winter in Shetland is nine in the morning. More than one Boxing Day I've come downstairs to find four or five men lying on the sitting room floor. And more than one Boxing Day Callum has been reviving himself and his cronies with the hair of the dog when I've driven with kids and excuses to my folks.

'Callum is sorry he canna make it, but he's full of da cold and he doesna want tae smit you.'

'Hah, I'll bet dat's not all he's full of,' my mother snaps. 'I don't know why you couldna hae come yesterday. Noo da bairns are getting deir presents late.'

'Dey don't mind, it makes Christmas last longer.' Colleen and Marianne run inside to find the cat.

'It's no da same,' my mother says, stamping around the kitchen filling a teapot. 'Boxing Day is for giving tae da poor, not tae your grandchildren.'

'It would be too lang a day for da bairns after dey've been through all Santa's stuff. You could come tae wis next Christmas if you want.'

'You ken we have animals to attend to.' As if to prove her right, my father comes hobbling past the window, carrying a bale of hay. 'Deir idder grandparents get tae see dem on Christmas day.'

So we go round in circles year after year, getting nowhere. It gives me a headache thinking about it. I realised when I came off the phone from Callum that he was right. Whatever way you look at it the pressure is too high. If we stay at home the drunks will come trying to drag Callum back into their pack. If we go to my folks for the entire Christmas day I just might turn to the drink.

I couldn't sleep last night for worrying. I rose about two and went downstairs. The kitchen fire was almost out, but I put on a few peats and sat slap against it trying to think. My knitting money used to go on necessities; now with Callum off the drink and in a good job I keep knitting so we can have a few luxuries. Last summer, for the first time since Colleen was born, we had a proper holiday. We had a cabin in the mountains in Norway; we swam in a lake, and took the girls on nature hikes. The holiday used up all my knitting money and more besides. It was a couple of months before I could begin saving again, so we can't really afford it, but this morning I rang Callum at his hotel. I told him to stay where he was, and then I made some phone calls. Maybe it's just running away, but we're off to Tenerife for Christmas, leaving the danger zone. As soon as the bairns get off the school bus there's a taxi coming to pick us up, and we're flying south, migrating like the birds. My mother flew in a rage when I rang her, and said she didn't know what I was thinking about taking the bairns away from their grandparents at Christmas. 'It's a time for families, Laura,' she said. 'You should be spending time wi wis while you still have da chance, not gallivanting halfway round da globe. We winna be around for ever you know.' His mother just said I was a selfish bitch, and slammed the phone down.

As I wait, watching for the school bus, I wonder if she's right. There's pecking at the window; it's a chaffinch that has been hopping about the garden all week, a straggler that forgot to fly south with the flock. I get some bread from the bin. It will be stale by the time we get back; he might as well have it. I put on my coat and go outside, tramping into the snow just as the bus pulls up. Colleen and Marianne tear the bread into pieces and throw it to the bird while I go back inside for the suitcases. Out of the corner of my eye I notice movement from the tree. The darkness makes it hard to see, but I want to believe the fluttering isn't a leftover leaf, but another bird.

Ian Stephen

BERNERAY and STORNOWAY
(from two drawings by David Connearn)

You cannot assume symmetry
in plotted curves of rise and fall

the upturn of tracings
on a calibrated sensor

a jaggy graph of soundings
hitting on a datum

passing it by.

A course can be corrected
in a compensatory swerve

transmitted by track-rods
which may tell their own story

gaining or losing.

You cannot transfer the template
from port to starboard frames

failing to allow for
the builder's eye on

particular planks.

And when a northwesterly freshens
over Staffin Island

you can term it offshore
considering that, on Rona,

an onshore wind is coming.

There is a bearing to join
St John's and Gallan Head

a simple reciprocal
affected by isobars

the stationing of satellites
recorded ephemera

hands on the helm.

Kenneth C. Steven

URNAIGHEAN

Chan eil càil ach brù-dearg is gealbhain
A' sgiathalaich mu sprùilleach arain, madainn na Bliadhn' Uir seo.

Os cionn nan craobh, tha adhar àrd gun chrìch,
Aon uinneag slàn, de ghlainne gheàrrte ghuirm.

Ach air taobh na beinn' ud thall tha'n Ruis na smàl,
Dràgan a' gleachd ri earball fhèin.

Air taobh eil' na h-aibhne, Serbia agus Bosnia,
An làmhan fhathast còmhdaichte le fuil is dusd.

An iochdar glinne, tha Arabaich na Boglaich a' sabaid
Gus nach bàthar iad fo smàig Irac.

Air na beanntan àrda, tha na Tibeatanaich a' gal,
Is Sine gam brodanachadh gu bàs.

Fo ar casan, trannsaichean na geur-leanmhainn,
Seòmraichean san Tuirc 's fo thalamh Chile agus Iran.

Ach air mo rèidio, chan eil ach an aon torghan:
Ciamar a tha dol dhan chluiche an gèam eile de chriocait.

Chan eil duine faicinn na h-aibhnichean làn fala,
No toirt paidhear chluas do ghlaodh an nàbaidh.

PRAYERS

Nothing else but the robins and sparrows,
Flurrying round crumbs this New Year morning.

Above the trees a cathedral sky,
One single window of cut blue glass.

But beyond the far hill, Russia is on fire,
A dragon fighting its own tail.

Just across the river, Bosnia and Serbia,
Their hands still covered with blood and dust.

Down in the valley the Marsh Arabs fighting
To keep from drowning beneath the might of Iraq.

High on these hilltops, the Tibetans crying
As China breaks them, one by one.

Under our feet, the corridors of the tortured,
The chambers in Turkey, beneath Chile and Iran.

Yet on my radio nothing but cricket;
The state of play in another game.

Nobody seeing the blood in the rivers,
No-one hearing the prayers of their neighbours.

Roderick Watson

BEYOND THE EDGE

I'm drawn to the moment on a blade when steel
fades out of self and into nothing, on a line
fine enough to defy even the gentlest touch.

There were seven chisels in my father's toolbox
laid top and tail about   like sardines
(or packed on their sides like bottles of wine)
yet each one different   suited and ground
to its own purpose   and buffed
to a misty mirror-finish on the flat.

Unused for years   they speak of when
preparation seemed all there was to do
and as important as the job itself
in the fight against encroaching dullness
with hands that shook on those clouded blades.
This was to be his last anthology of sharpness.

Each chisel was taken to the limit
honed on a strap   and then laid by
keen   to make even the dullest timber
flower – some other day perhaps.
I took them home and use them now
– and now and then I sharpen one. Thinking

nothing cuts forever. Thinking
of a molecular discrimination so refined
that you would feel nothing should the finger
slip to bone – beyond surprise
at how the blood has come to marry oil
on the cold black stone below.

So we work to carve shape from sense
trembling in the confusion of the wild woods
out there – where my father went to live
altogether away from sharp edges.
With a toolbox ready for every single thing
but that which came to pass.

THE SCHOOLS OF SIENA

1. *Crossing to Tuscany*

Watching the cars go by the Motor-Chef
– the white lights coming and the red lights
going away – penetrated by my daughter's hair
falling into her sleepy seven-year old eyes
– penetrated by the instability of things ...

Teachers charted atoms at school (like bricks
in a builder's yard baked with dust on Helen's eye
or weighted with trees and Wordsworth and all)
they never told us we were the sky: bricks books
yard school wall – all riddled with light
or rocked on the airwaves passing through
without a pause – like ripples from a stone
dropped into the throat of the first well ...

The motorway went to a place where Dante was
waiting at the top of a round and rugged hill
(everything so green) 'Ah yes' he said
'It is like that but later burns to umber
under the sun. It comes close to us that star's face.'

(So the symbols gather standing in the snow
I keep to the back of my mind to make them out
and know them as my own – like the children
in a white garden beside a thin snow tower
who wears a carrot for a nose and shares
a coal-black ferocious grin with both
of them   and me   and you.)

Now we are south and into August. On the terrace
above olive trees and fields of blackened sun flowers
ants ferry crumbs across the tiles; at our feet
they make a double chain as each one halts
to check its fellow before it starts again:
to and fro   to and fro   to and fro.
Electric lamps burn at night   memories   wired
to each gravestone outside the village walls.
Rain spots fall from a clear blue sky.

In the afternoon things stop. We try to sleep
through waves of heat and thunder   and lie apart
in bed   attentive to a cataleptic sky which talks
only to itself   in language of purest force.
Heavier and heavier   we sweat and itch
in the shade of old rooms with massive thwarted beams.
We dream of reaching light and snow   but tender dust
drifts down to teach us after all   how we go.

2. *Towards the Sun*
    (in the gallery)

Our Lady of the Cherries   applauds
the baby with his fists full of fruit.

Our Lady of the Sparrow   inclines
her narrow head to the cheerful bird.

Our Lady of the Milk   suckles
one abstracted   hungry   little god.

> Her eyes are as clear as scalded almonds.
> Her skin is virgin olive oil.
> Her face is as pure as the face of a cat.

I look at: thinness of gold leaf;
a small town burning on the hill beyond;
the weight of nothingness   those blue heavens.

3. No. 1 Via d'Ingresso

Black swifts pinwheel round the square
and fix us to the ground.   They never
stop weaving their nets in the air.

Yet we found them unexpectedly as if
parked in corners   dead birds
neat   specialised   stiff.

We threw those sleek bodies over the wall
– where rosemary grows in a sweet
haze   of turpentine and menthol

– where the quick electric lizards meet
and the ants sustain their endless chains
around the passion flower   around our feet.

4. The Life
(at the abbey of Monte Oliveto Maggiore)

Our brother   who is white as a blanket
gives us milk-white chocolate to eat
lays his tender and hairless hand
on my son's blond head   tenderly
as his lips make a kiss on the gift to say
his silent blessings on us all
who stand still for them.   Cold   dry
sunlight   sifts from the cloister wall.
San Bernardino is mending broken pots
again – a canny miracle barely
fixed on Signorelli's fresco of humble ghosts.

In the Chapel (two hundred years later)
baroque and fruity muscular forms
strain   and vault into empty air and
eternal   hemispherical   space. We stand there
and I think of the poor clay below
and the narrow brick road we walked
worn hollow by our hosts' bony feet.
I think of raw wooden stakes   nailed
by wires to the milky horizon   waiting
for tendril vines to rise and cling.

The early fields are veined with poppies
in the cool air.   Once there was nothing
here.   The lesson is still emptiness.

We take our blessings with us.